The Healing Power of Champagne

History, Traditions, Biology and Diet

Dr Tran Ky and Dr F. Drouard

Translated by Reginald Duquesnoy

SAVOIR-BOIRE LTD

Published in 2006 by Savoir-Boire Limited
www.savoirboire.co.uk

ISBN 0-9554105-0-9
ISBN 978-0-9554105-0-5

Printed in the UK by Butler and Tanner, Frome, Somerset
Designed by Springboard Design Partnership, Bristol, UK

Contents

Technical appendix

'Take good care of the body,
so that the soul may enjoy its abode.'

Saint Francois de Sales (1590)

Introduction

While books about wine and champagne abound, this particular work by Dr. Tran Ky and Dr. Drouard addresses a somewhat more unusual and specific aspect of the beverage, not as a mood-enhancing tipple, but as remedy, healing potion. *'Le Vin Medecin'*, champagne as doctor. A recurring theme ever since wine was invented and history recorded, but somehow better explored by the French, as befits the living embodiments and proponents of the art of the paradox.

As with any human production and undertaking, wine, like Aesop's fabled tongue, can lead to the best and the worst.

With the birth of alcoholism in the 19th century, before it was called less threateningly, intemperance, the French authorities have now swung the pendulum the other way and in a bout of repressive and exacerbated puritanism are proposing to burn what was previously adored by ushering the same opprobrium upon wine as is cast on tobacco in England and the United States

In England, meanwhile, 'binge drinking', the suicidal annihilation of the senses, is reaching epidemic proportions. Excess seems to be a sad trait of human nature but amplified by globalisation, mass culture and a curious phenomenon of bad behaviour resonance.

To our knowledge, champagne, the universal symbol of joy and celebration has rarely been linked or associated with drunkenness. A 'feminine', soothing drink, as some are fond of qualifying it, always seems to bring out the best in us. This book examines how it can also put the best back in us.

Dr. Tran Ky and Dr. Drouard review the science of this wonderful mechanism, this quasi-alchemic process, whereby the many and multiple beneficial active molecules of a good champagne interact at the most basic cellular level with our affected organs to remedy the ailments which afflict all of us occasionally.

Paradox supreme and highly counter-intuitive, who would have thought that a sip of champagne and its pearly bubbles, cures all windy manifestations: burping, hiccups and flatulence. But there you are! Who knows that a glass of 'champers', judiciously timed, will enhance your libido better than any pill while preserving the romance.

'Half a bottle of champagne is worth half of Harley Street', noted the astute observer. So we are delighted to let the genie out of the bottle for the benefit of our English-speaking readers.

The other message and the leitmotif of our good doctors is that the therapeutic effect of champagne only works in moderation. As in homeopathy, the potency of the remedy is inversely correlated to its dilution. Less is more! The healing unit of measure, the flute, the enchanted flute, to put the sparkle back in your eye, is one and one only, and not a drop more; per meal, that is. That is the prescription; what puts *'mens sana in corpore sano'*, the healthy mind in the healthy body. Go beyond and enter not in totally uncharted waters, but operate then in a different mode without the blessing of medical authority. Even the formidable Sir Winston Churchill, who 'took more out of alcohol than alcohol took out of him' bowed to the iron law of diminishing returns: 'A single glass of champagne imparts a feeling of exhilaration... A bottle produces the opposite.'

This is also the time and place to tip our hats and raise our glasses and make a libation to the English, the Frenchman's best enemy, without whom champagne would never be what it is today. To them we owe the toast, the cork, the bottle, the corkscrew and last but not least, champagne brut, dry or extra-dry, to match their wit.

As the second biggest consumers of the nectar, after the French, we will eternally be 'grapeful' to them.

Messieurs les Anglais, tirez les premiers et...

Reginald Duquesnoy

'O Father Noah, who didst plant the vine'
Francois Villon 'Ballade and Prayer'

Foreword

Noah, having survived the Flood, grew the vine. The great Judeo-Christian mystery of origins makes the beginning of history coincide with the planting of the vine and the making of wine. What a symbol! According to the Talmud, it was God Himself who revealed to the patriarchs the secret of wine making. In Greek mythology, wine was indeed a gift from the gods. Dionysus, the son of Zeus, stole wine from the Persians to give to the Greeks, who proclaimed him God of wine.

Noah got a wee bit tipsy and some of us have followed his example ever since. But wine, and especially champagne, the subject of this book, has also contributed more than its fair share to man's happiness and to his health.

Historically, the vine emerged on earth well before man. It was already blooming over sixty million years ago, awaiting our arrival. In Champagne, in the porous terrain of the tertiary in the region of Sézanne we find fossil vine imprints. This *vitis sezannensis* was wiped out in Europe a hundred thousand years ago by the great Riss glaciation. Nevertheless, during the Neolithic period early man began harvesting the fruits of *vitis vinifera*, the species to which the modern vines of Champagne belong.

Where and when did vine cultivation begin? The oldest written and iconographic records of organised vineyards go back to 2500 BC and come from Mesopotamia (Iraq) and the Nile Valley. And the Champagne region itself? We know that the Romans created an important vineyard in Narbonnaise Gaul in the first century BC but Julius Caesar did not in fact find the Marne hills covered with vines because they were not cultivated in Champagne until the end of the 3rd century as an extension of the Burgundian vineyard.

Wine has been used therapeutically, both internally and externally, from the beginning. '*Wine is wonderfully made for man's needs, in health or illness, if one drinks it wisely and moderately, according to the individual constitution.*' (Hippocrates)

For a long time this use was governed by experiment and experience, but in modern times the therapeutic use of champagne has evolved into a reasoned and scientific therapeutic practice, which will be dealt with at length in the main body of this book. The introductory chapters will present champagne, a breed apart in the wondrous world of wines, and an overview of its use since the end of the 17th century to maintain and enhance man's health, as well as cure some of his ailments. For the more scientifically inclined reader, two annexes delve in greater detail into the complexities of champagne production and the intricacies of champagne absorption.

'The whole universe concentrated in this wine'
Apollinaire

CHAPTER 1

Champagne Past and Present

Until the end of the Middle Ages the Champagne region produced wines of little merit: light red clarets for the most part. But, in the 16th century, the wine of Ay acquired a European reputation. Francois I, Charles V, Henry VIII, Pope Leo X and Henri IV maintained their own agents in this town next to Epernay to procure this highly prized wine. However it was only around 1600 that the overall quality of the wines of the province improved to match those of Beaune in Burgundy and they acquired the name 'Wines of Champagne'. They were served not only in Reims at the coronation of the kings of France, but also at most European courts. Champagne became the daily table wine of Louis XIV as well as William III of England.

In the second half of the 17th century the champagne makers succeeded in stabilizing their wine, making it easier to preserve. By using a special press process, they managed to produce a highly desirable white wine from red grapes. Dom Perignon, cellarmaster of the monastery of Hautvillers, improved it further by artfully crafting an *assemblage*, a blend of grapes of different origins.

It was also around this time that wine started being sold in bottles instead of barrels. Some winemakers noticed that the alcoholic fermentation continued in the bottle and that, as a result, a bubbly froth appeared spontaneously when the bottle was opened. It is thanks to the collective realisation of this new phenomenon that champagne came into being, at the end of the 17th century.

"How is champagne made?"
"By sheer genius sir, sheer genius."
(overheard at White's Club, London)

Barely noticed at first, champagne soon became the rage at the court of Phillipe d'Orléans, the Prince Regent. Kings, emperors, and the whole European aristocracy, with the enthusiastic support of literary men like Voltaire, Diderot and Goethe, adopted champagne as the wine of feasting, *par excellence.* In 1729 the first champagne houses were created in Epernay and Reims.

For centuries, winemaking had been a matter of trial and error; now it benefited from the technical progress of the 19th century. From three hundred thousand bottles a year at the time of the Revolution, production increased to six and a half million bottles in 1845 and to nearly thirty million bottles a year at the end of the 19th century. Since then production has increased exponentially, reaching close to three hundred million bottles in recent years, of which nearly half are exported.

In 1927, champagne became an *Appellation d'Origine Contrôllée.* This title certifies that the wine is made from grapes grown in a specified champagne area and cultivated according to strict regulations. The only grapes allowed are Chardonnay, Pinot Noir and Pinot Meunier and the yield per hectare is limited. These regulations ensure the excellence of the grapes. Quality is always the first priority. Further restrictions apply to the pressing process. The champagne itself can only be made in Champagne through a second fermentation in the bottle, and there is a minimum age at shipment. The controls on the entire process are tight and highly efficient.

Champagne-making requires the same process of fermentation as any non-sparkling white wine. Each year's *crus* are blended with reserve wines from previous years to obtain a harmonious blend finer than the sum of its parts and characteristic of the wine maker, whose 'signature' will be recognisable in the personality of his brand. After they are blended, the wines are re-bottled with the addition of sugar and *champenois* yeasts. In this second fermentation the yeasts transform the sugar into alcohol and form a carbonic gas which remains in the bottle to form the bubbles the consumer sees rising in his glass. This 'froth formation' takes from eight to ten weeks and the champagne is then left to mature for about three years (though the minimum requirement is only one year!). Before shipping, the winemaker eliminates the deposit left by the yeasts by freeing the cork. The pressure in the bottle forces the sediment out and sugar is then added to obtain the extra-brut, brut, extra-dry, dry or semi-dry wine.

Champagne is not a wine for laying down; it does not improve with age, though it keeps well if kept on its side and protected from heat and especially light, which is most harmful. Once opened, the carbonated gas stays in the bottle, provided it is re-corked immediately. If drunk for therapeutic reasons, it might be preferable to opt for half or even quarter bottles.

Champagne dispenses a mellow euphoria. It is by choice the wine of celebration, but it is also good company - always. When one is lonely, or languishing in a hospital bed, the golden bubbles gently rising in their myriads in the glass induce a gentle mood and a sense of wellbeing, drowning the worries of the morrow.

'I drink champagne when I am happy, and when I am sad. Sometimes I drink alone. When in company, it is an absolute requirement. I dip my lips in a flute when I am not hungry and I drink it when I am hungry. Otherwise I never touch the stuff, except when I am thirsty.' (Lilly Bollinger)

'He, who knows how to taste,
does not drink but samples secrets.'
Salvador Dali

CHAPTER 2

A brief history of the medical use of champagne

Well before the wines of Champagne became sparkling, their beneficial effect and the important role they could play in the maintenance or recovery of good health were already well known. As early as 850 AD, Hincmar, Archbishop of Reims, advised his friend Pardulus, Bishop of Laon, to heal himself by drinking the wines of Epernay and Mailly.

'The Art of Healing', 1674, recommends the wines of champagne as those 'which least encumber the stomach'. Saint-Simon notes in his 'Memoirs' that Duchesne, physician to the king's sons, lived to ninety-one years of age and *'maintained to the last a state of perfect health and a clear head by supping every night on a salad and only drinking champagne wine. He highly recommended this diet.'* Canon Godinot in his 1718 treatise on the wines of Champagne writes: *'Of all wines, none is better for health than a grey or rose wine of Champagne. It is so light that it flows and passes through much faster than any other wine in the kingdom. Contrary to popular belief, it does not give gout. In the province, nobody suffers from it. Is that not proof enough?'*

However, in the 1650s, the Burgundians began to worry about the increasing success of champagne and the doctors of Beaune become its fierce detractors. There were counter-attacks from the faculty of Medicine of Reims, which bravely defended its home product and presented evidence to support its health benefit claims. Thus began the Wine Quarrel, an astonishing, often acerbic debate which lasted ...one hundred and twenty years! Champagne wine had become the effervescent wine celebrated all over Europe and Burgundian envy knew no bounds. In the early 1700s, a flurry of poetic interventions, odes in praise of burgundy and champagne, turned the quarrel into a literary fracas rather than a scientific debate. Contemporary journals published claim and counter-claim, producing citizens of both Reims and Beaune who had managed to live to the canonical age of 118 by drinking their local vintage! But the doctors continued to stand fast on the health benefits of champagne. In 1730, Master Jacques, the King's physician in Epernay, wrote to Monsieur Helvetius, ordinary doctor to the King and first physician to the Queen, extolling the benefits of the non-sparkling champagne: *'It is a matter of certainty that the good wine of Champagne, white, non-sparkling, drunk in moderation when mature and cut with more or less water, is the most appropriate liquor to maintain good health, and the only one which can be tolerated, or even advised in most maladies.'*

Gout - the curse of the bon-vivant

The quarrel even rippled across the Channel. In 1775, in 'Observations, Historical, Critical and Medical on Wines', Sir Edward Barry wrote: *'The wines of Champagne are light and generous; once they have aged sufficiently, they become very salutary. They do not induce either gout or stones, contrary to common belief: for amongst the inhabitants of this province these disorders are rarely encountered, although they drink the wines most liberally.'*

And the economist Arthur Young observed in his 'French Travels': *'I suppose the carbonic gas is good for rheumatism; I was a bit suspicious before entering Champagne, but the sparkling wine cleared all up.'*

The last word in the Wine Quarrel belongs to Jean Claude Navier, Doctor-Regent of the Faculty of Medicine of Reims, who defended his 'Memorandum on the usage of sparkling wine against putrid fevers and other diseases of the same nature' before the Schools of the Faculty in 1778. He said:

'Because champagne contains less tartar than other wines, it is less likely to cause gout or kidney stones. It is the least inflammatory wine because there is less spirit alcohol. In addition to these precious qualities which the sparkling wine shares with the other wines of champagne, it contains in addition a constituent ingredient that the chemists call "gas" or" trapped air"; this constituent ingredient is its defining characteristic and is recognised today as the most powerful antiseptic existing in nature and an efficacious dissolver of kidney stones. The delicious juice of the Champagne hills thus has a dual advantage. It is both incontestably the most agreeable of all wines and also the best adapted to the wise laws the Creator has laid down for the conservation of health and life. The wine of Champagne can dilute

thickened humours, clear obstructions, provoke urine, stimulate expectoration, fight anemia, ward off gout and destroy stones, and protect against epidemic diseases.'

As medicine developed, practitioners took an increasingly scientific interest in the therapeutic effects of champagne. In 1817, Dr. Loebenstein-Loebel, Professor at the Faculty of Medicine of Iena and sanitary advisor to the Duke of Weimar wrote 'A Treatise on the usage and the effects of wines on dangerous diseases' published simultaneously in French and German. He writes:

'Thanks to its sugar content and carbonic gas, the wine of champagne produces an excellent effect on digestion: drunk frothing it breaks down acidities in the primary passage, tones the organs and brings about calm and joy in melancholic and hypochondriac patients. We use it with good results in the following conditions:

i. In the case of idiopathic vomiting due to a nervous disease of the stomach or of the intestinal tract, we administered, either every half hour or every hour, a quarter or a half glass of the best champagne, and increased the dosage every two hours, up to a full glass.

ii. In morning sickness, when vomiting becomes debilitating and continuous, and there is a risk of miscarriage, the use of champagne both internally and externally was of great help.

iii. In kidney stone attacks, and even in the case of calculus pain in the bladder, we obtained an alleviation of the pain after using champagne, as well as more copious urine. But in these cases one must administer high doses: one can start with a full glass, three to four times a day, but can go as high as three glasses each time.

iv. In chronic gout affliction, as for instance gout in the feet, we employed champagne with great success.

v. When treating these diseases one must use the best champagnes and one will reinforce the chances of success by employing one known as oeil-de-perdrix.'

The idea that champagne has therapeutic powers appears in German literature as well. Hoffman, in his 'Tales' maintains that champagne is a sovereign remedy for young women's headaches and a 'salutary medicine' providing a 'most peaceful night without the slightest hint of a bad dream.'

In another tale, a doctor prescribes to his patient *'a certain frothy drink hermetically sealed in its bottle, as the medicinal drink was brought, everybody wanted to sample the remedy to support the patient. Hoffman swallowed the potion without the slightest hint of repulsion, with a resignation, which provoked the admiration of those present, much reassured about his condition.'*

In France also, doctors praise the health benefits of champagne claiming that *'The sparkling champagne and all wines charged with carbonic acid, awake the digestive function, stimulate the mental faculties, inspire cheerfulness and a sweet disposition'*.

In the second half of the 19th century the oenologists took up the baton from the medics. They agreed that champagne was 'wonderfully digestive', thanks to being saturated with carbonic gas, and that it had power to stop vomiting induced by nervous irritation. But they also believed that it was efficacious against infectious diseases like yellow fever, cholera and typhoid. The 'Larousse Médical', in 1920, reported that recent work by Sabrazez and Mercandier showed that 'the wine of Champagne destroys the bacillus of typhoid fever in ten minutes'. This astounding anti-infectious property of champagne seems confirmed by the following anecdote

told by Arsene Houssaye in his memoirs: '*I was the victim of a typhoid type of fever; I was on my last legs. But the dying can have remarkable hearing: I overheard my doctors in a corner deciding that I would not last the night. When they came back to my bed: "My friends", says I," if depart I must, you will not object to a last bottle of champagne..." Between eleven o'clock and midnight, when the four doctors came back, they were somewhat surprised to see me ready to get up and go. The champagne had saved my life.*'

At the end of the 19th century the association between champagne and health developed. The wine of golden bubbles took its place in the pharmacopoeia. To underline its beneficial effects champagne was labelled 'fountain of youth', 'health-giving champagne', 'convalescents' tisane', and recommended on medical authority. At a time when dosage was very important, some very dry champagnes, like Laurent-Perrier's '*Grand Vin sans sucre*', were marketed for diabetics. One finds champagne in the military hospital pharmacies of many armed forces, and military doctors report favourably on its therapeutic use. In the National Army Museum in London you will find two half bottles of champagne with a label which reads: '*Selected by Her Majesty's War Office for the hospitals and the soldiers wounded or taken sick during the Boer campaign.*'

During the First World War certain champagne houses publicised themselves in their brochures as 'suppliers to the military and civilian hospitals'.

Some went even further. They produced champagne with a medicine, introduced before the final corking. Thus one finds available in pharmacies amongst the trade names registered in 1898, a Quinine Champagne, a Bipepsin Champagne and a Pepsin Champagne. A Eupeptic Champagne was sold with an instruction manual and a Dispepsia and Eupeptic Champagne came with the following prescription:

'*The Eupeptic Champagne of Choubry Brothers contains one gram of pepsin per flute, or per ten centilitres of wine. One should take note of this high medicinal*

Toast to women's liberation by some already seriously liberated women.

THE CURRENCY QUESTION; OR, THE STOCK EXCHANGE OUT FOR THE DAY.

Jones: "I say, Brown, things are deuced bad in the City."
Brown: "Then I'm deuced glad I'm at Epsom."
(from a drawing by John Leech in 'Punch')

concentration in order to avoid overdose. A dose of one flute after each meal is largely sufficient for an adult. Notwithstanding this relatively high quantity of pepsin, the taste of the champagne is in no way altered.'

Champagne has always done its share to maintain man in good health and there are many illustrious testimonials to its virtue. To give two examples: Escoffier, the famous chef, recounts in his memoirs how he once asked Sarah Bernhardt the secret of her legendary energy. She said: *'The main thing is will power, sustained by an excellent champagne.'* Escoffier continues: *'Madame Sarah Bernhardt regularly drank a half bottle of Moët et Chandon with each of her meals and she told me that the effect of the champenois froth acted upon her in the most marvellous fashion.'*

Sir Duff Cooper in 'Old Men Forget', tells us that whenever his father, a doctor, saw him take any kind of tonic, he would say: 'What this boy needs is a pint of champagne and a couple of mutton chops.'

A number of experimental investigations were done in the 20th century into the therapeutic benefits of champagne. Let us mention those of Dr Monceaux, whose findings were published in 'Dietetics and Nutrition', December, 1951, under the title: 'The role of champagne in post surgery diet', and those of Dr Guénard whose paper: 'The use of champagne in surgery follow-up', was communicated to the First Congress of the International Medical Committee for the Promotion of Wine in 1935. On this occasion, Dr Guénard underlined the use of champagne during delivery *'to quench thirst and ease the strain'*, a view reinforced by the work of Dr Siguret, obstetrician of the Faculty of Medicine of Paris in his treatise entitled 'The effects of champagne after childbirth'. Gynaecologists' interest in champagne is not new if one is to believe 'Charivari', a satirical journal, it is true, but one which reports in its issue of 1st May 1852 that, due to a poor harvest, there has been a shortage of champagne so severe that 'the wine merchants are rationing bottles to one per person. To get two, one needs a prescription, or be a lady in an interesting condition'.

From 1966 to 1969 a team of investigators from the Faculty of Medicine of Reims researched the influence of champagne on breathing. They found that: *'The respiratory equivalent, which measures the volume of air needed by the lungs in order for the subject to absorb a litre of oxygen, diminishes under the influence of champagne. In other words, one breathes more efficiently'.*

Finally, the beneficial effects of champagne are always highlighted in most medical books devoted to the therapeutic virtues of wines in general. Thus, champagne has always, since it first bubbled forth, lent assistance to medicine for the greater benefit of mankind, besides being 'the quintessential wine of civilization'. (Talleyrand)

'You do not drink, you give a kiss
and wine gives back a caress.'
Montaigne

CHAPTER 3

Champagne therapy as an alternative

One need not probe far beneath the superficial, occasionally gaudy, and always hedonistic face of champagne in its modern guise to reach the paradox between it's public face and its actual inherent character.

The effervescence, the delightful and quasi-iconic glow as light hits the elegant flute is its style; the rich content of mineral salts, vitamins, trace elements and other organic compounds absorbed by the vine and released in its juice, are its soul. Champagne constitutes a life-sustaining beverage endowed with undeniable dietetic properties, well deserving of its historical use as a beneficial dietary supplement and beyond that, with judicial and careful consumption, as a medicine, able to alleviate many of the ailments of everyday living.

Yes, your eyes do not deceive you – champagne as medicinal tonic! What a splendid idea! Makes you want to succumb to illness on the spot... Yes, a surprising notion in the light of current thinking with regard to alcohol. But which has considerably more merit than the interest we bestow upon the torrent of dietary and health fads, a by-product of the modern obsession for the 'quick-fix'.

The medicinal consumption of champagne is not a 'fad'. Nor is it a cheeky 'alternative' that seeks to inhabit the polar extreme of theories held by modern, 'established' medical creed. The therapeutic use of champagne is arguably more historically established in principle and practice than any facet of modern medicine that we allow to so dominate our approach to health. Let us look to ourselves, and the style of our culture and living, if we wish to understand why the propositions within this book appear so surprising to conventional wisdom, at first glance. For 20th century culture has moved us steadily away from the first precept of healthy living: 'everything in moderation'. Excess permeates contemporary life yet we all know that when moderation is abandoned all substances, including champagne, become toxic to our being. It is the homeopathic principle of the minimum dose that illuminates the theory of champagne therapy. Thus, have we allowed the blameless medicine to be miscast for the consequences of our own misuse.

Truly, there is no such thing as a single therapeutic approach; there are ethno-medicines, traditional medicines, popular medicines and modern medicine, all of which have sought to ease suffering since the dawn of time. None can claim a monopoly, although some do, over our well-being. The art of healing should be a broad church and accommodate many branches. In the end there is only one Medicine at the service of all.

Today, micro-analysis allows us to study the constituents of champagne at their molecular level and thus move closer to understanding how this wine works

The Philantropists of the day

The 43rd toast to temperance...

Mr Edward Cousin, QC: "*Do you drink champagne yourself?*"
Mr Oscar Wilde: "*Yes, iced champagne is a favourite drink of mine – strongly against my doctor's orders.*"
Mr Edward Cousin, QC: "*Never mind your doctor's orders sir!*"
Mr Oscar Wilde: "*I never do.*"

within the labyrinth of our bodies. We are able to explain its effects, beneficial or not, on such and such a symptom and receive insight into how our ancestors discovered and refined their medical knowledge and technique. The medicines of the past have something to teach us. To attempt to understand them is more than an obligation; it is an encounter with our own roots.

To continue treating ourselves as we did in Moliere's time would of course be absurd. Such medicine was undeniably not always highly efficient! But then, truth be told, neither is ours, and tradition deserves both our sympathy and our curiosity. In the light of how medicinal champagne theory has been lost and distorted, perhaps its study can point us even further towards a lost style of living, where moderation was understood and implemented as a path to health.

This is, of course, not to shine the light away from the evolutionary process that has lead medicinal practice to its current state in which exhaustive diagnostic ability and radical treatments do save lives that would otherwise have been unquestionably lost in yesteryear. But let us begin to consider the effect of champagne on our organism that made our ancestors recognise it as a tonic not merely for the spirit, but also for the body, long before the age of technical medical excellence.

We know well enough the consequences of intemperance with any alcoholic drink on our being. The molecule ethyl alcohol, like some present day anaesthetising drugs, possesses a double action with contradictory effects. In small doses it induces euphoria by stimulating the brain to release neurotransmitters. When our consumption exceeds our ability to absorb it, this hormonal secretion can have an anarchic effect on the body. However ethyl alcohol is but one of champagne's many components. A number of its constituents has been shown to act specifically on certain organs or tissues. In a more general way, the properties of certain of its vegetable essences are similar in effect to those used in aromatherapy. Its organic and mineral essences justify its role in oligo-therapy, a practice that uses individual trace minerals for therapeutic support, supplementing the necessary minerals for enzymatic functions and considers its remedies as catalysts that speed up metabolic rate, and nourish the vitality at a cellular level. The complex mechanisms, which underpin the biological effects of champagne shall be elucidated further on in this study. The focus will not be on the intoxicating qualities of champagne, when consumed with abandon, which we know only too well, but on its long discarded role as remedy and healing potion.

Its merit derives undeniably from its carefully crafted physio-chemical balance. With a low pH, it is an acidic wine, which even when too young, does not irritate the stomach, however sensitive. Its carbonic gas content derives solely from the second fermentation, very different from other sparkling wines, most of which are brutally conditioned by artificial gas injection. In champagne, carbonic gas dissipates naturally and, quite paradoxically, shows itself capable of relieving those affected by bloating and wind. There is a grace in the process of its birth, a uniqueness in its naturally occurring ethereal bubbly phenomena that seems to endow it with some healing quality that cannot be replicated by man-made copies. Of course, as in all wines there are some harmful substances also present in champagne. However they only appear in trace amounts and do not manifest their toxicity as they are quickly flushed from the system as long as one drinks in moderation and keeps to the pace of the body's digestive rhythms.

Champaign driving away real pain

Champagne has been sidelined by the advent of modern medicine, but popular tradition remains faithful to a time-honored friend, and rightly so. Health is our most precious gift, and as George Bernard Shaw sagely noted that 'Youth is wasted on the young', so might we say that 'Health is wasted on the well'. But good health faces an amazing array of threats, a number that seems to grow rather than diminish in the dazzle and pace of the modern world, pushing our boundaries ever further. So must medicine and therapeutics develop and push at their boundaries; but with this expansion of knowledge and tireless search for new understanding in pursuit of the art of cure, let us remember to look back and treasure what wisdom and knowledge is our inheritance, those therapies that relieved the pains of our forebears who weren't so very different from us. And if alternative champagne therapy has but one thing to teach us from our past, let it be that we never forget that after all 'In Vino Veritas' but also 'Sanitas', as we shall review; ultimately, a certain type of truth lies at the bottom of the bottle, so lets not go searching too far for divine truths and medicinal wisdoms when a sparkling glass has so many secrets yet to reveal...

'Bring wine, boy! bring flowering garlands to me!
Yes, bring them, so that I may try a bout with love'
Anacreon

CHAPTER 4
Stimulation of Desire

'We do not accomplish anything specifically human unless desire is involved.' Desire is the necessary passage for every feeling which invites us to the feast of life; the prelude to every embrace. Desire is a permanent revolution which burns in each of us, the spur which drives us to reach beyond ourselves.

Paradoxically, the birth of desire, like the trigger for sexual tension, does not simply depend on the presence of male or female hormones, as is the case in animals. The sentimental and sexual behaviour of humans obeys some very complex mechanisms in the brain, to which the hormones are mere accessories. The work of hormones is accomplished with discretion and patience but leads to a sudden burst.

In humans the blossoming of desire is subject to all sorts of inhibitions. It can be unsatisfactory either because it is too rapid or too long; either because it is isolated from other phases of sexual and sentimental behaviour; or because it is not shared on the psycho-affective and socio-cultural levels.

The absence of sexual desire in women is widely described: one speaks of indifference, apathy, or lack of sexual interest. Libido, the sentimental and erotic impulse, can be eroded or even extinguished. Amorously solicited, the woman does not necessarily fail in the accomplishment of the sexual act, but performs without pleasure. The causes of this phenomenon remain shrouded in mystery. Some speak of constitutional factors; of internal conflicts; of rebellion or frustration; or even of frigidity. Estimates of the frequency of this condition are vague and fantastic. Depending on the sources, it varies from 2 to 40 per cent in the groups of women surveyed. Or, if one were to believe the French national bard, Georges Brassens, 95 per cent of the times women are bored 'stiff', so to speak, in the land which has made 'Ars Amatori' (The Art of Love - Ovid) its bedside reference book. Surely, exaggerated poetic licence.

There is not a shadow of a doubt that socio-cultural and psychological factors play a fundamental role in the arousal of passion. It takes remarkably little to overcome inhibitions. Casanova made love to innumerable women and inspired their passion by inviting them to drink champagne, which made them madly amorous. Champagne flowed freely at the court of the Regent, Phillipe d'Orléans, and at the court of Louis XV. The Duke of Richelieu wrote that the courtesans of the Regency Court *'presented a scandalous chronicle of human manners; the orgies only began when one and all had reached that state of joy which is procured by the wine of champagne'*. Some have claimed that Madame de Pompadour, whose temperament was reputedly cold, drank champagne on a daily basis to maintain the

Opening Shot

pace of her frolics, and she herself affirmed that champagne was the only wine 'without dangers for the beauty of women'. After La Pompadour's death, the new favourites of Louis XV claimed that wine was the only remedy capable of animating the monarch's ardour.

In the mysterious world of love, men and women react differently. If the sexual and erotic stimuli received by a woman are not given sufficient value by the

Skirmish

psycho-affective context to generate the necessary emotional charge, desire may not blossom. Gynaecological problems, blood disturbances, fatigue, irritations of all kinds (lack of sleep, sedative abuse), are all capable of dulling female desire in an otherwise problem-free subject.

Despite great progress in understanding physiology, we do not know that much about the biology of love. Are we talking about a social reflex or an instinct?

Surrender

'Ma femme, aux épaules de champagne...'
'My wife, with champagne shoulders...'
André Breton

Through which effect can such an impulse push an individual beyond himself? The little we do know is only the tiniest part of this unfathomable mystery.

Research has tried to understand the basic causes responsible for initiating sexual behaviour in higher animals. Animal experiments have demonstrated the existence of a highly complex system of reflex circuits triggered periodically by

Joie-de-vivre

'Do your best, and keep in a state of joy'
Spinoza

hormonal stimulation. Biologists have discovered the circuits of sexual pleasure, and possibly even orgasm, in the brain. But the real centre of desire, where motivation and tension interact to trigger sexual arousal, remains hidden.

Could it be that the trail of desire will be found in the study of hormones, which play a part in the magic of sexual gratification? Dopamine, one of the chemical molecules our nerve cells use to transmit their electrical messages, is found in above average quantities in the networks of passion. The alchemy of hormonal organisation may be fundamental to the arousal of amorous behaviour; but we must not forget the importance of culture in the awakening of feeling. In every case the two go hand in hand: biology provides availability, while the psycho-cultural spark brings enchantment.

Often, when a man presses his partner with tender solicitations, 'at last, after many hesitations, circumlocutions, vague hints, he finally understands what she was too delicate to say', champagne steps in to overcome indecision. *'The shortest distance between a man and a woman is a glass of champagne,'* said a wit. Thanks to its magic, barriers fade, distances diminish, tongues loosen and flesh vibrates. Words, once confused, become clear. That is the sublime moment when surrender occurs.

Under these circumstances, one must relish the spell of champagne, which fuses the thirst for the other with the sudden irruption of desire. Art and Eros lurk in this most spiritual liquid.

Their fusion exalts the Self to sing the praises of the Other. Eroticism generates deep, intimate, inexpressible joys, while art conveys its own enchanting and affecting emotions. The two encourage the passions to bloom and bring perfect understanding between the lovers. The splendour of champagne revives the flame of emotion. Like a symphony, the wine brings forth an immediate understanding and initiates a fiery intimacy, which overcomes initial reserve.

The song of love is always humming within us. Without regard to race, colour, class, champagne, the equal opportunity provider, though frail and ephemeral, is above all happy, fraternal, rich in spirit and joy. It carries a message of gaiety, sincerity and lucidity. It shows us that feeling is the music of the body and soul.

But whatever the power, strength or charm of this wine, whether it tempts, awakens, soothes, consoles or calms, one must never sacrifice the principle of moderation.

The influence exerted by the pressure of our socio-cultural environment on our intimacy is much more marked than we suppose. These social constraints, unique to our species, have always led our fellow men to devise all kinds of stratagems to overcome obstacles standing in the way of courting the partner of their choice. Champagne can transform timidity to daring, caution to generosity, the moment into eternity. The aromas of champagne can overcome prejudice, destroy doubt and ennoble the moment. When all possibilities have been exhausted and one remains indecisive and powerless, champagne adds the sparkle. The internal clock of amorous experience is ticking; its call is irresistible. Love needs the poetry of fantasy; it is guided by the sweetness of imagination. Insensibly, feelings take wing, soaring on the fairy bubbles, the foam of dreams and desire, chanted by Hoffman.

The time has come to scrutinise in detail the mechanism of this explosive inspiration.

'Plaisir d'amour ne dure qu'un moment;
Chagrin d'amour dure toute la vie...'

This popular song, so dear to our grandmothers, is out of fashion now. Our society does not value sadness and sentimental frustration, although they are more prevalent than ever because of the many barriers raised in a world, which claims to be one of communication. Psychoanalysis seeks to combat sadness as some kind of malady by all sorts of means, even chemotherapy. But in the age of the computer, the chemistry of love still intrigues us. Our sentimental life, as we have seen, depends more or less on the electro-chemical activity of the brain which responds to external stimuli. The differences between the many ways of being and loving must correspond, at least in part, to individual biological nuances.

Substances which have an effect on the psyche, and notably champagne, do not by themselves create affective reactions, let alone romance. They only contribute to the development of a pre-existing feeling present in a latent state, ready to germinate and bloom. These substances can also decrease feeling or disturb it when absorption is inadequate. They resemble emotions which push the brain to elaborate substances, either activating or dulling the circuits controlling feeling. Nearly all the vicissitudes of life depend on the biochemical secretions of the brain. Both the pleasure and the pain of love result from the activity of this alchemy of felt emotions.

The unconscious energy released is transformed into attraction and attachment. It is the unforgettable moment when lovers together do all sorts of mad things, make every promise, accept every invitation, dare all. During these delicious moments, pleasure and desire are from time to time revived by new stimulations aimed at rekindling the initial euphoria. At this stage anything which might hamper the flowering of feeling only serves to reinforce it. The fluctuation of hormones and electric waves, as well as the dynamics of bodies, introduce new sensory excitement to harmonise the couple. Over and beyond abandon and the gift of self, love also needs the charm of fantasy and of the unexpected.

Occasionally, that miracle hangs on a few drops of love potion which call upon the magic of hormones and their neurotransmitters to create a state of euphoria for a few hours; time enough to shed taboos, drop barriers, and open the way to the game of love and hazard.

One should keep in mind that all substances produced by the brain have a dual power. They control the activity of the pituitary gland: a small gland at the base of the brain whose hormones encourage the other endocrine glands. They also help to modulate, transmit and interpret messages received. These hormones react on the brain which secretes them in a symbiotic interplay. So, there are several levels of interpretation. The interaction of effect and response is reflexive, under internal and external stimuli. The subtlety of this equilibrium is so delicate that any excess of champagne will throw it into jeopardy.

The fool who seeks to reinforce his sense of well-being by increasing his consumption will quickly exhaust his reserve of neurotransmitters. The weakened brain will not respond any longer in the proper fashion; this would be a shame when the whole being should be at its best.

The effect of champagne seems to be directly tied to its speedy action on the hypothalamus, where the amplified release of all sorts of hormones, notably dopamines and sexual hormones, takes place.

But always avoid excess. More than one flute for a woman, two for a man, and the magic is gone. In truth, lovers did not wait for the discoveries of science to appreciate the power of this wine in awakening and sustaining their emotions.

*'Without a flûte
How to reach
The true self?'*
Li Chang Fang

CHAPTER 5
Obesity and Cellulite

Nothing is more changeable than the aesthetic ideal or more confusing than the canons of feminine beauty. Our ancestors who built cathedrals, admired pale women with slender limbs and firm breasts, whom they often represented as angels. From the Renaissance onwards taste preferred beauties in full bloom with tender flesh: *'A round neck and bosom too, both white as snow; full breasts wide and white, two round firm apples which swing to and fro in small undulating movements; arms fleshy and rounded. This is the ideal and perfect example of the true and artless beauty of woman.'*

Joan of Aragon, thought to be 'the most beautiful of beauties', was immortalised for her 'wide and rounded hips, wide bosom where no bone is to be seen, and (her) complexion full of vitality'. Ronsard in his time sang of the 'generous bosom' of his beloved, like buxom hillocks, and praised them for being altogether large, full and deep. Titian, Tintoretto and many other Venetian artists painted mostly plump and succulent beauties: *succulentae.*

Rubens' 'Three Graces' display opulent, generous, tender flesh. Of course, at times, one judged some beauty too fat. But nobody found excessive weight ugly or undesirable in itself; on the contrary, too much 'muchness' could be extremely seductive, and no one would have found a slim woman attractive. Those who were not fortunate enough to have accumulated a certain *'avoir-du-poids'* were thought incapable of inspiring love.

The poet Giambulari went as far as advising young men not to marry slim girls who would be 'like a drying rack in bed, with skin so coarse that they seem to wear a hair shirt'. Woe to women who did not possess breasts like 'twin pinnacles of thick creamy milk' so the poet could calm his ravenous 'hunger' and feast on the charms of the beloved, who for him is a 'repast', a 'dish', 'juice', 'wine', 'nectar', 'honey'.

Until the beginning of the 19th century women were indeed afraid of losing weight. They followed all sorts of recipes to add weight. Glissanti, in his 'Moral Discourses', wrote about Venetian women so anxious to gain weight that *'they procured nuts from India, almonds, pistachios, pine nuts, melon seeds, then pressed them together with sugar to make some sort of marzipan!'*

There are even secret recipes, stuffed with feminine jealousy, designed to slim down rivals! In any case, according to contemporary observers, women did not seem to object to the masculine tastes, which imposed these aesthetic canons. This attests to the obsession we have with being beautiful. Nowadays our notions of the aesthetic operate according to the same principles, though the criteria are radically different. Our times celebrate tanned and skeletal models. The essential thing (the bottom line!) for most is not to be beautiful, but to be 'where it's at'.

It might be useful, for those who want to slim, to first understand what causes obesity. To begin with, the propensity to accumulate fat depends on the genetic make-up of the individual, as each person reacts differently to food. Children born to obese parents will have a propensity to add weight, unless they are brought up according to a well-balanced diet and way of life.

Conversely, someone who shows no tendency to put on weight might think he can eat anything while, in fact, the fat content of his blood would increase if fat and sugar are consumed in excess. It is well known that subjects who complain about their excessive weight often eat less than normal, are always hungry, and still put on weight.

In general, obese people suffer from poor regulation of body temperature, which is controlled by the hypothalamus. In a cold environment they are unable to convert their fat reserve into energy quickly. That is why many of them are cold sensitive and feel the effects of the slightest temperature change more intensely. One can, of course, remedy this deficiency by recommending physical activity or hydrotherapy, but a balanced diet is the indispensable basic treatment, whatever the nature or multiplicity of factors underlying obesity: psychological, social, cultural or biological.

Despite the great progress made in biology, we still do not know much about the intimate life of fatty tissues. For a long time we have underestimated the extraordinary physiology of this reserve tissue which enabled our ancestors to survive the Ice Ages. Our fatty cells, the adipocytes, possess the amazing faculty to store surplus nutrients in order to protect us against shortages and famine. During a prolonged period of food deprivation only those subjects who have sufficient fatty reserves at their disposal can ensure their survival. It goes without saying that in rich countries the omnipresence of supermarkets and a sedentary way of life has rendered the necessity of keeping fatty reserves redundant.

The adipose mass represents from 15 to 25 per cent of the weight of a normally constituted individual, a percentage, which can double in an obese person. Fatty tissues are generally more developed in women than in men, a difference partly explained by the ovarian hormones, oestrogen and progesterone. Indeed, some contraceptive pills bring on unexpected weight gain, even if the woman has maintained a normal diet. This is unfortunately a frequent side effect for women using this contraceptive method. One in five women gains weight after a few months on the pill. Some thin women may derive great benefits from the pill as the hormones aid the harmonious development of the silhouette, but others expand out of proportion regardless of the type of pill prescribed. The mechanism of weight gain is very complex.

In addition, obesity always aggravates pre-existent cellulite; it can also produce it directly in the presence of contributory factors like smoking or frequent sunburn. In effect, cellulite is a modification of the texture of the sub-cutaneous connective tissue which thickens and becomes granular, sending a shiver down the spine of pretty women. Although the phenomenon is initially localised in the hips, it progressively affects the belly, thighs and arms. The skin loses its elasticity and becomes painful under pressure.

Normally, a supple and uniform connective tissue supports the skin as a sort of double layer, which is what confers natural elasticity. The physical properties of the elastic fibres are behind this wonderful aspect of the skin, so pleasing to the eye and so pleasant to touch. The skin is equipped with extraordinarily sensitive sensory

Geometry of love

receptors. This deep, tactile perception varies according to sex and individual. Women are much more sensitive to touch than men. Touching plays an absolutely essential role in the non-verbal communication of affection. For this vital organ to function properly day and night, it must be continuously nourished and irrigated by a rich network of blood vessels. The lymphatic system supplies the blood vessels and removes waste. When we speak of circulation we think of veins and arteries, which carry blood, but rarely of lymphatic channels, yet their own role is paramount.

Muscular activity and sufficient absorption of water are usually enough to get the lymphatic system going. Physical activity increases the drainage capacity of lymphatic circulation by fifteen times. Half a flute of champagne also effectively raises the rate of circulation as well as promoting elimination through diuresis. Of course, this is no reason to neglect physical exercise. Even elderly people who might be confined to bed through sickness or infirmity should practise some form of movement as recommended by their physiotherapist.

Excess or hormonal imbalance, regardless of origin, can provoke an abnormal blood viscosity, increase the lipoprotein content, augment water retention and thicken the venous walls. In brief, it creates all the conditions for cellulite, the female Achilles' heel, to take hold, especially if the person concerned smokes or neglects the basic rules of a healthy diet.

'My cure is all in wine...'
Olivier Basselin

It all starts with a slight increase of lipids in the blood. Most often excessive fatty food in the diet is to blame for a given level of blood viscosity. In fact cellulite progresses fairly slowly. It is entirely possible to diagnose, prevent and treat in time. Cellulite is difficult to detect in young, sunburnt women because the skin is tender. But in those who abuse tobacco and sugar, cellulite appears as 'grapefruit peel' skin, waterlogged and fatty, slightly rubbery when pinched. It expands insidiously from the belly to the waist and thighs.

Sometimes cellulite can take an alarming turn. Swelling occurs mainly after sunstroke or as an allergic reaction. Then one must act rapidly before the skin hardens with fibrous scarring. If the victim is still young he or she can be helped as long as the skin remains supple. A balanced diet, physical exercise, less exposure to sun, a low oestrogen pill, and an end to tobacco abuse are enough to reverse skin degeneration. But it will promptly reappear if the bad habits recur. It is as if the cellulite beats a temporary strategic retreat but lies in ambush ready to pounce at the first opportunity. That is why preventive measures remain, in practice, the only treatment.

In many cases, after pregnancy for instance, the subject notices that her weight increases over a few months, perhaps exacerbated by the wrong kind of pill. Fat increases and the skin starts to stretch; it is important to act quickly to nip this in the bud.

Age generally brings a loss of skin elasticity. In this case cellulite is very insidious. It takes a soft form, characterised by a reduction in elastic fibres. Treatment can be long, but relatively successful. In fact, the difficulty is not treating the cellulite, but knowing when to stop. Once melted, the fat which distended the skin leaves a flabby, inelastic cover, which is even more unattractive than the initial cellulite. That is why it is just as important to stop untimely treatments as to treat the initial cause of the problem. If the skin is truly loose and sagging, cosmetic surgery might provide a last-ditch solution.

To beat cellulite and 'save one's skin,' early detection is essential. There are many therapeutic methods available. Year in, year out, over six billion euros are spent in France to treat this condition. Modern methods include ionophoresis, mesotherapy and rejuvenating wraps to melt away the undesirable mass. Ultrasound, water jets, air pressure, heat chambers and lymphatic massage can also improve drainage. Finally, the laser is reputed to be one of the best methods science has for removing fat. Initially, its impact is sensational. Under its thermal magic the coarse skin becomes smooth again. Miracle or magic? What is really involved is a loss of plasma from the capillaries, a sort of oedema. If pushed too far this treatment can severely damage the skin. Exotic treatments like acupuncture or Chinese breathing methods are less expensive but probably no more effective. The best approach is probably a combination of a healthy diet, sufficient physical exercise and hydrotherapy. We should drink enough water, about two litres a day and avoid tobacco, too many pills and too much sun. Tradition further recommends poultices of creeping ivy or kelp, horsetail baths and infusions of birch leaves, which our grandmothers swore by.

Recourse to champagne brut, one glass per meal, is also recommended because of its diuretic properties and ability to stimulate the lymphatic system. The wine will not make you lose weight, but represents an interesting adjuvant treatment in the initial battle against cellulite.

Colette, who loved '*grande cuisine*', always used champagne in a recipe she is said to have inherited from George Sand, and that is how she maintained her svelte figure until she was eighty-one years of age. Moderation is the name of the game. Champagne, in this context, is considered as a remedy which must be treated gingerly and respectfully and not quaffed down in vast quantities as during a banquet.

'Be moderate in order to taste the joys of life in abundance.'
Epicurus

CHAPTER 6

Appetite Loss

'There is no better natural doctor for a man than his own appetite.' Rousseau was right. Every man in good health has an appetite at meal times. The hypothalamus, the lower part of the brain, is the centre of appetite and thirst, and also of satiety. All the nerve centres are interdependent and subject to the control of the cortex, the supreme authority, the thalamus, a sub-layer which acts as a moderator, and the limbic system, seat of memory and emotion. All these layers exert their influence on the hypothalamus to shape the deep appetites.

The complex organisation and integration of the brain allows for the development of psychological and sensory factors which can have a direct bearing on the functioning of the deep centres of hunger and thirst and alter the sense of need. Champagne liberates these nerve centres from the restraint exercised by the upper layers of the brain.

A few invisible molecules suffice to abruptly awaken appetite. For humans, unlike other animals, eating signifies much more than simple nourishment. Our eating behaviour is determined by our social and cultural organisation, with its conditioning, preferences, rhythm and rituals. If humans manage, thanks to their technology, to make their food, they are themselves shaped, more or less unconsciously, by foods charged with energy, affectivity and symbolism. The complexity which results therefrom, bears witness to the high degree of liberty and choice humans have in their eating behaviour.

The role of emotion during a meal is concentrated in the limbic system. There, nerve formations either check or excite appetite. For instance, one is inclined to eat more at a banquet, less when eating alone. The participation of the cerebral cortex during eating is naturally preponderant, even if it is not the seat of hunger and satiation. Through learning or conditioning, the brain is able to modify in a thousand ways the nuances of our eating behaviour. Only humans are capable of intentionally suspending the desire to eat. These peculiarities, inherent in our species, highlight the importance of psychological and socio-cultural factors, which constantly influence our response to food.

We have been taught since early childhood to associate emotion with the taking of nourishment. Nourishment is always associated with the mother. We understand that the smell and sight of food is inextricably mixed with feeling. Nourishment signifies love, security, appeasement and encouragement for the child, while its absence or insufficiency provokes reactions of anxiety, anger and frustration.

The rhythm of meals contributes to structuring time and space for the child. It imposes and fashions the alternation of hunger and appetite. It is one of the first ideas instilled in children All of these daily experiences have created in our memory the taste or distaste for certain foods. These references constitute a vast network of mostly unconscious symbols and prejudices. The more rigid the personality, the tighter their hold.

Hunger is a physiological sensation which signals the need to consume food when blood sugar levels fall. Appetite, on the other hand, is a psycho-cultural propensity, which draws us toward a particular food because of its nature, preparation, presentation or known organoleptic qualities. This desire foreshadows the pleasurable sensations that the coveted food will deliver.

Hunger and appetite are thus two different, but closely linked, sensations. Both participate in the growth of sensory and psychological arousal. They are frequently confused in our eating patterns. If one can eat without hunger, it is also possible to experience no desire for food even when the sensation of hunger is present. If the sensation produced by these two states disappears, the situation can become serious, as in anorexia.

Other factors also make their influence felt: one will eat more if the food is delicious and the company convivial. These socio-cultural and psycho-emotional influences make it very hard to understand how champagne acts on the nerve centre to trigger appetite. Does it act by stimulation or by blocking the blockages? Whatever the reason, champagne is as good an appetite stimulant as most remedies prescribed for that purpose.

In man, the effect of champagne occurs about ten minutes after absorption. The wine imitates the action of dopamine, which slows the control from the centre of satiety and opens appetite. The physical and chemical contact of the food with the digestive tract is also a quick way to inform the brain about the quantity of food absorbed. This near-instantaneous evaluation works much faster than the elevation of the rate of blood sugar which is relatively slow. The carbonic gas in champagne follows this mechanism by stimulating the secretion of the stomach glands and opens the appetite. To work effectively, the wine should not be too cold or too green. The optimum temperature should be between six and nine degrees.

It is interesting to note that popular medicine has always used champagne to combat appetite loss without actually knowing that the wine acted as a neurotransmitter stimulating the activity of the hunger centre. Daily experience over three centuries has established the exceptional quality of the wine as an aperitif.

Empress Josephine used it liberally to settle her capricious stomach. She had a fondness for Moët and attempted to share her inclination with the Emperor, who found it did, indeed, help sustain his appetite. Although he was himself a devoted Chambertin drinker, in recognition of services rendered, he decorated Jean-Remy Moët with his own *Legion d'Honneur* in 1814, just before the grand finale.

Napolean decorating Jean Marie Moët.
"I need champagne in victory and in defeat."

CHAPTER 7

Arterial Stenosis

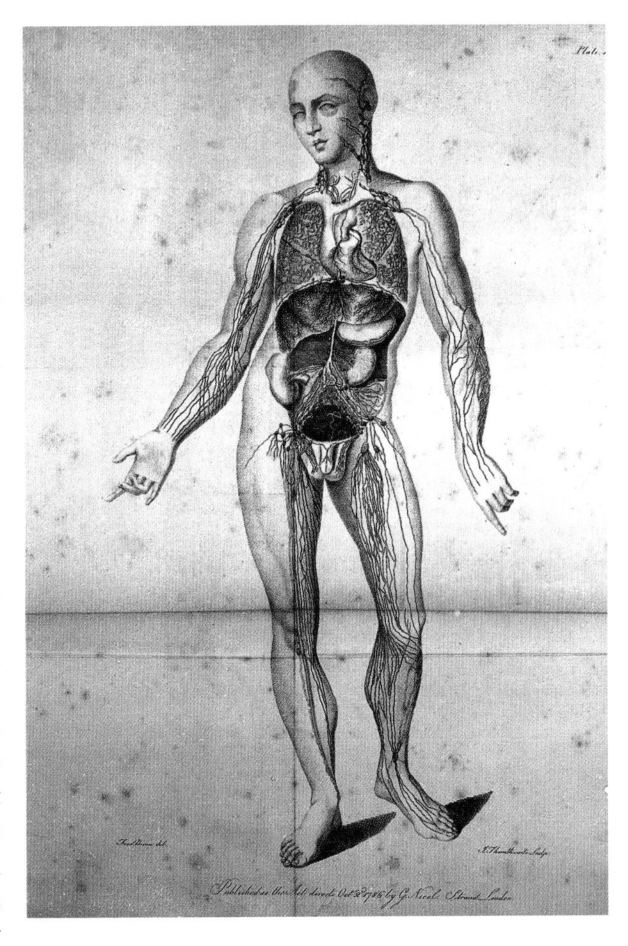

Arteries, like veins, have a wall composed of three concentric layers; the intima is the innermost and made of endothelial cells, which are directly in contact with the blood.

The endothelial cells are the seat of an intense activity all along the ninety-six kilometres of circulatory system piping. Any anomaly in the functioning of these cells can lead to stenosis or vessel obstruction which leads to thrombosis. Tobacco, alcohol, diabetes, infections, intoxications and an unbalanced diet high in fats and sugars are predisposing factors which lead to deposits on the artery walls and clogged circulation.

To keep our channels healthy and combat the thickening of the arterial walls it is important to maintain the precarious balance under which our precious endothelial cells have to work. A recent study shows a slight correlation between even modest consumption of wine and incidence of cardiac problems due to circulatory inadequacy.

Furthermore, epidemiological surveys in Western Europe have highlighted the importance of one trace element, selenium, whose function is to safeguard the biological integrity of the endothelial cells. The surveys reveal that myocardial infarction strikes more often amongst subjects where the blood concentration of selenium is abnormally low. In these cases, if the subjects also smoke and have a diet high in sugar and saturated fats, arteriosclerosis is inevitable.

Thanks to its anti-oxidant property, selenium plays an important role in immune defences. Our endothelial cells constantly require its support in order to neutralise all kinds of toxic waste which tends to accumulate on their surface, blocking their secretory capabilities. Champagne, in homeopathic doses, helps these asphyxiated cells breathe better while ensuring the regeneration of their membrane.

The structural alteration of the heart and the blood vessels happens progressively and discretely, which is why the damage is already well advanced when an attack occurs. Because of their vulnerability to toxins and microbes these organs must be treated with great care. Simply avoiding tobacco, excess sugar and certain types of fat is already a great help. Biology has demonstrated that the heart is more than a mere pump, as formerly thought. It is in reality an enormous endocrine gland secreting a variety of hormones, which intervene in the activity of the kidneys, the adrenal glands, and the centres which regulate blood pressure.

This fragile mechanism is often paralysed by nicotine, but purged by the biological substances present in champagne. That is why popular medicine has always advised against red wine for diseased arteries while authorising the sparkling white one, in small doses, to regulate the work of the circulatory system.

'Wine gladdens the heart of man,
and joy is the mother of all virtues.'
Goethe

CHAPTER 8

Migraine

History is full of famous migraine sufferers. From Saint-Louis to Bonaparte, Cervantes to Tolstoy, Darwin to Bernard Shaw, Madame de Maintenon to Queen Victoria, the list is long. Tolstoy and Shaw took champagne to ease their attacks, though it did no more than other more conventional treatments. To make migraine more ordinary we love to cite examples of celebrities who suffer from it in order to console ourselves for the inherent injustice of a biological make-up that condemns us to this malady. The occasional intense headache did not prevent these illustrious personalities from pursuing their uncommon destiny.

Pascal used to illustrate the pains he felt by drawing telling sketches in the margins of his manuscripts. Schiller put apples in a drawer; the perfume of the fruit was the only thing that soothed the intense piercing pain of migraine. Lewis Carroll found the inspiration for 'Alice in Wonderland' during a long night of migraine. This character, which sometimes grows beyond measure and then shrinks to the size of a mouse, came out of the premonitory symptoms, which preceded and announced the imminent arrival of the storm in his head. Lewis Carroll enjoyed his therapeutic champagne, but found the relief it procured unreliable and unpredictable. Be that as it may, it was still the most pleasant and least harmful remedy to fight the malady.

Balzac, in the 'Physiology of Marriage', thought the affliction was a feminine affectation: *'The affliction, which they can use in a variety of ways, is migraine. This indisposition, the easiest excuse because without apparent symptom, only requires these few words: "I have a migraine".'*

To look upon these painful manifestations as a simple exercise of seductive power is a little reductive, even if the idea is charming. But it would be wrong to think that a woman would push coquetry to the point of intentionally bringing on a migraine. The times have gone when women needed this type of artifice to seduce or keep at bay the over-enthusiastic lover. Although some persist in believing that the disorder is one of those unfathomable manifestations of the psyche, most researchers lean increasingly towards looking into the biochemistry of the brain to understand the intricacies of this phenomenon.

An erroneous but persistent view has it that migraine is the result of a certain snobbery dictated by socio-cultural pressures. Barthès wrote that he had *'taken up the habit of saying "migraine" for "headache" (perhaps because it had a nicer ring). This inaccurate word (because it was not only half of my head that suffered) is a socially unjust word: the mythology attributes migraine to bourgeois women and men of letters... Of course, working people suffer from migraine just as much as chic ladies.'*

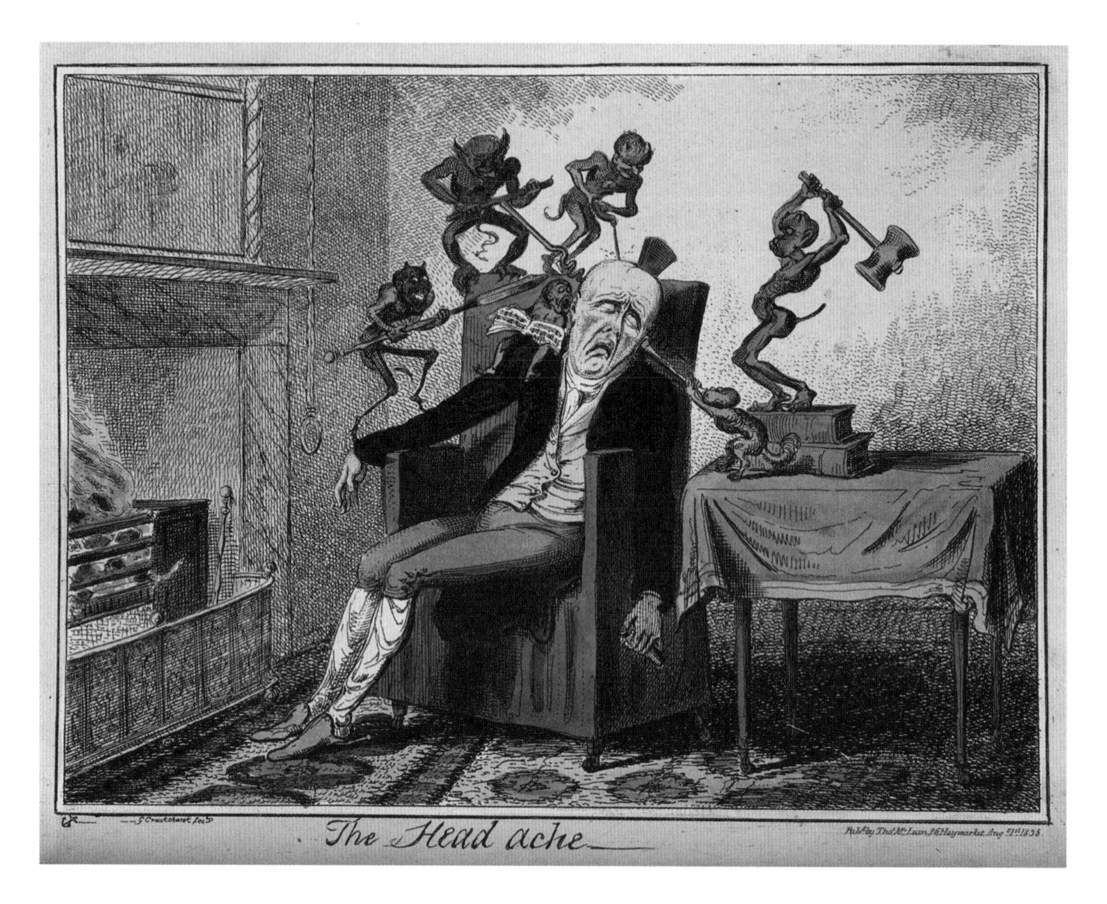

What matter if to bed I go,
Dull head and muddied thick
A glass in the morning
Sets me right very quick
Champagne Charlie

The splitting headache has nothing to do with beautiful manners. On the contrary, poor working conditions, noise, poor lighting and poor ventilation accelerate the appearance of these crises and increase their frequency. We know that migraine has long resisted any form of therapy and that remedies are numerous but ineffective.

Progress in understanding the causes of this affliction has been desperately slow because it is so difficult to reproduce experimentally in animals or men. It is almost impossible to reproduce in someone who does not suffer from migraine. This hints at a biochemical anomaly, or a certain individual or genetic susceptibility, at variance with classic laws of heredity.

We know of a few biological substances produced by the organism which could cause this painful symptom: the serotonin in blood platelets, prostaglandins, histamine and several other normal secretions of our cells, but they do not produce migraine in non-sensitive subjects. Research in this area increasingly shows that in certain subjects the enzyme system is too weak to neutralise undesirable substances which the organism produces or absorbs. Experiments on animals require a very high dose of the incriminating substances to obtain the unusual behavioural pattern, which could resemble migraine. And these biological substances are present, in their normal state, in the organisms of even the most seriously affected sufferers without producing any reaction outside the crisis period. Could there be a sudden excessive discharge of these substances? Does the internal wall of the blood vessels suddenly change to react differently to substances which are normally present in the blood? These are the kinds of questions which might eventually lead to the solution of this puzzling enigma.

In reality, there is not one migraine but many, and it is no exaggeration to say that every sufferer has his or her own. The unpredictability of these attacks and the uncertain results of treatment, whatever remedy is used, seem to characterise this capricious affliction.

If there are so many methods and medications aimed at mastering this condition it is because no single one has been capable of addressing all types of migraine or adapting to the changing circumstances of its manifestations. Taking into account the disconcerting results of the various treatments, some have postulated a relationship between these incurable migraines and latent character troubles. In fact, in some unexplained cases, a placebo suffices to halt the onset of an attack. This ambiguity results from the very nature of the affliction whose causes are multiple and remain confusing, despite all the research in disciplines such as neurophysiology and the biochemistry of the brain. This underlines the importance of treating the whole mental and physical constitution of the patient once the pain has been relieved. It is clear that each individual case is marked by its own specific biological, psycho-emotional and socio-cultural features which must be considered in devising an appropriate solution. The efficacy of the therapeutic intervention depends on this fundamental aspect of treatment dictated by the multiplicity of causes, manifestations and individuals encountered.

Migraine remains a baffling phenomenon but advances in research are slowly but surely reducing the unknowns. The support that biology and medicine can offer to migraine sufferers is now quite substantial and not limited to simply relieving the pounding pain it brings. The ambition of the ongoing work is to elucidate this mysterious phenomenon and discover preventive measures, which would nip it in the bud at the first sign of an attack. The little we already know opens many avenues which allow us to claim that this affliction is partially conquered, despite the many remaining questions still unanswered. With patience and tenacity every discovery adds to our knowledge of the intimate life of the vessels and cells of our brain. Science is more and more interested in this symptom, which strikes indiscriminately without regard to social standing.

In England, it is estimated that 10 per cent of Her Majesty's subjects suffer from migraine. The percentage is more or less the same for most European countries and for North America. On average, one man in seven and one woman in four is affected, more or less frequently.

The medicinal virtue of champagne for migraine comes partly from its high lithium content and it is probably the synergistic mechanism of ions that popular medicine relied on to alleviate the pain. The action of lithium is reinforced by the presence of magnesium ions, which we know have a sedative influence on the brain.

It seems that under the wine's influence a discharge of enzymes takes place which hastens the elimination of the catecholamines (adrenaline, noradrenaline,

Migraine - the ultimate cure

dopamine) although relief is variable. Moreover, this popular remedy only works in the early stages of migraine, signalled by precursory signs such as pins and needles, abnormal vision and digestive problems.

Paradoxically, migraine is not something the organism easily succumbs to, as it is endowed with many security checks and barriers. The monitoring system of the brain is incredibly fine-tuned and it is only at the end of an extremely unusual set of circumstances that such a circulatory disorder can happen. Our body has a whole array of corrective mechanisms, which are on permanent duty to avoid any mishap in this incredibly complex bit of machinery. And it is precisely this complexity which provides security, as it offers multiple solutions to confront shifting situations.

Champagne can, sometimes, help relieve migraine by boosting the control network of the moderating neurotransmitters and their receptors located on the cells with a contribution of trace elements and energy. Champagne is the only wine to have this beneficial property; other wines have a propensity to aggravate the condition and even trigger it. Sufferers know this well and usually avoid wine, whether white, red or rosé, but make an exception for champagne, which does not affect them, and, occasionally, helps prevent the onset of a crisis. The reason is that champagne contains very few flavonoids. These elements are progressively digested by the second fermentation, and become less numerous as the champagne ages and matures. So, good quality champagne is not only able to relieve a headache, it can also stop lurking migraine at the onset.

That property, empirically observed, has led to the time-honoured advice to sip a little champagne to quieten or shorten a migraine. No other remedy is as pleasant, even if it is a little expensive and not yet available on the NHS.

Clinical experiments published in 'The Lancet' allow us to better understand why some migraines triggered by the absorption of wine disappear after physical exertion. Muscles are our enzyme banks, and by producing a sustained effort at the beginning of a migraine we activate circulation in the muscle tissue where the enzymes cleanse the blood and neutralise some of the noxious substances responsible for the attack. The experiments also drew attention to the action of certain digestive substances capable of reaching the brain circulation either to aggravate the headache forming there or to remedy it.

Through its wealth of mineral elements, especially in the ionic state, champagne supplies energy materials which can be rapidly used to re-establish balance at the level of brain cells, either by filling a void or deficiency, or by opening channels so that the ions can re-supply the depleted neurons. Its healing virtue is probably exercised via this energetic bias which corrects the disturbed cellular function. We do not claim that champagne calms all headaches - that would be going too far - but its efficacy is well-documented, and recent research sheds further light on the underlying mechanism of its activity. And taking a sip of champagne to avert a migraine does not prevent using other forms of treatment as well.

André Malraux was a notorious sufferer of migraine: '*Migraine, this horrible affliction; migraine which tortures like no other torment ever has, which crushes the head, drives one mad, scatters ideas and blows memories like dust on the wind, migraine got hold of me.*'

After he had tried a bevy of remedies, anxiously seeking an end to the splitting pain, which racked his brain, the author of 'La Condition Humaine' finally found solace in a glass of champagne.

The times are past when one had to accept this fate in silent resignation. Nowadays the discovery and development of a number of specific treatments allow sufferers to liberate themselves from this spectre.

'God, in His goodness, sent the grape
To him both great and small;
Little fools will drink too much
And great fools none at all.'
Anon

CHAPTER 9

Insomnia

Unfortunately, many of us suffer from sleepless nights. Some suffer so much they begin to think that 'insomnia is the only heroic attitude in bed'. Beyond doubt, the steam engine and electricity have contributed to the growth of insomnia. In the past, to sleep and to dream have always been highly ritualised activities. Amongst primitive peoples as well as in ancient civilizations, immutable rules governed sleep. The soul (or the breath) of the sleeper left his body to wander in another world inhabited by ancestors, divinities, and the spirits of the clan. That is why one should never awake the sleeper, for fear his soul would get lost or return to the wrong body. This underlines the fundamental place that mental images and dreams occupied in primitive religions. Does modern man really escape from the influence of these traditional beliefs? Why must we sleep? An Amazonian legend provides one explanation:

'At the beginning of time the sun was fixed in the sky and men never stopped working. Dead tired, they decided to acquire sleep from the Lord of Night. He granted their wish in the form of a small box which they were not to open before returning to their village. Driven by curiosity they opened it on the road. At once, night sprang out and plunged the forest into darkness. Only when the men reached their home did things fall back into order. From then on, time was equally divided between the light of day and the darkness of night. And men could rest and work in fair proportions....'

The moral of this myth lies in its praise of harmony between man and nature, which should be celebrated with special rites. Most people surround their sleep with well-defined precautions designed to derive the maximum benefit from the period of rest. Thus they fix the period of sleep, its precise duration; they define special locations and prescribe certain postures for sleep. Under the Tuareg tent, for example, custom requires men to sleep on the northern side, women on the southern. Despite the excruciatingly long polar night, Eskimos strive to maintain a regular alternation of activities. Their sleep patterns follow the daily movement of the moon and stars. Humanity has always taken thousands of precautions when entering the world of the night in order to find deep and peaceful sleep.

Sleep is a great source of creativity for many poets, artists and scientists. The great German chemist, Kekule, solved the enigma of the molecular structure of benzine during a dream. The archaeologist, Hilprecht, found the key to the translation of the stone of Nebuchadnezzar in his sleep.

The oneiric universe is undoubtedly the Eldorado, the promised land where

the sleeper finds his inspiration. Stevenson credited the idea for 'Dr Jeykll and Mr Hyde' to his dreams. Byron loved to drink a glass of champagne before retiring to sleep. The most beautiful verses of 'Don Juan' were apparently written after a sojourn in the realm of Morpheus. Byron liked to recommend champagne to his insomniac friends as the only remedy capable of banishing nightmares and sadness. Thomas Edison, Raymond Poincaré, Paul Doumer also knew the remedy and used it to counter their insomnia. Relieved of crippling sleeplessness, they managed to solve the many problems which preoccupied them.

As things stand, we know little about the mysterious world of sleep. Despite all efforts, we still do not know why we sleep. It is a difficult subject to study because man is the only animal to complain about his sleep. Perhaps, like Proust, we should be resigned: 'A little insomnia is not without use, if only to better appreciate sleep.'

At present we don't really understand sleep and dreaming, but everyone agrees that sleep and dreams are indispensable to our health. Even a sleep marred by nightmares is refreshing and does not prevent the brain from restoring itself to face another day.

As it happens, a person complaining of insomnia does in fact sleep as evidenced by the electric signals recorded during his sleep. But, unable to dream, his sleep is incomplete and superficial and not integrated into his consciousness. It seems that many cases of insomnia are, in fact, this failure to integrate psychic material through dreaming.

There is another kind of insomnia, perhaps the most frequent, which is triggered by a lag in our biological rhythm. Instead of wanting to sleep at 23:00, some must sleep at 13:00 or 17:00 or, on the other hand, cannot sleep till 2:00 in the morning. This dislocation in the hours of sleep impacts on the working day. Sleep disturbance becomes a serious problem when the beginning of a sleep period after a sleepless night coincides with the time when you are expected to start your day. One can imagine the difficulties of someone who is unable to reconcile his sleep-wake cycle with his social and professional responsibilities.

Occasionally, poor irrigation of the deep layers of the brain is sufficient to suppress or delay deep sleep. As a result, the sleep integration mechanism fails and when the sleeper wakes he does not experience the rested sensation of having had a good night.

Many forms of insomnia are caused by over-stimulation. Too much coffee or tea, too many cigarettes are frequently responsible. A healthy lifestyle and adequate exercise are all that is needed to restore balance and improve the quality of sleep.

Paradoxically, it is during periods of wakefulness that the brain manufactures the substances which will lead to sleep and conversely, while we sleep our nervous system prepares the chemical cocktail needed to wake up. Neurobiologists have long searched for the chemical molecules, secreted by the brain, which induce sleep and dreams. They thought the brain produced a hypnogenetic or sleep-inducing substance; whereas in fact the substances produced during sleep prepare our waking! The brain creates its sleep while awake, and the dynamics of wakefulness while asleep. The insomniac, instead of preparing his sleep, is occupied with the activities of wakefulness. Curiously, we will one day find the key to the kingdom of dreams in the study of our waking state.

We all know the famous painting by Greuze, 'The Lazy Boy', showing a child asleep on his open book. Far from lazing about, the brain of the child is memorizing what he has just learned. During sleep, phosphorus, which synthesizes the protein molecules which fix memory, is activated. Sleep is the secret craftsman of memory.

In some cases, superficial sleep is characterised by jerky movements of the limbs, sleep apnea, startled awakening and violent coughing possibly due to swallowing problems. These symptoms indicate that insomnia is not merely subjective and may require medical examination.

It even happens that a lucid brain repels any idea of rest: *'Before sleeping one must put one's thoughts to rest,'* writes Alain in 'Putting Your Mind to Rest'. *'But there is a problem; to put a thought to rest requires thinking, and to think is to awake. Every thought puts us on alert: that is perversely natural.'*

It is precisely in such an absurd and unreasonable situation that the author appreciated the saving repose procured by a little good champagne. Jean Cocteau also recognised the merits of this wine, always ready to unlock the gates of the kingdom of dreams.

This magical property of champagne, to induce sleep at a sip, is due not only to its magnesium, copper, ionic iron and calcium, but also to the specific properties of its higher alcohols and zinc. In general, about one hour after drinking a glass of champagne, the solitary insomniac begins to yawn and feels an irresistible urge to fall asleep. That is why tradition quite rightly recommends to those suffering from insomnia to drink a glass, or half a glass, of champagne after an evening meal, in lieu of sleeping pills. This usually leads to a peaceful night and an energetic awakening. No need to drink more, lest one oversleeps.

Over and above this immediate effect it has been observed that the zinc content of champagne is truly remarkable. A small flute of this wine provides up to 7mg of this trace element, one of the essential mineral elements in grape juice. The brain is also an enormous hormonal gland and consumes a fair amount of this metal in ionic form.

In many cases insomnia is mostly a temporary phenomenon arising from a sudden change in environment, a room that is too hot or too noisy, or triggered by a psychological shock. As a rule, sleeping remedies should only be used in cases of absolute necessity and for very brief periods. Tranquillisers are sometimes preferred, but they should not be administered for longer than a month to avoid establishing an insomniac state dependent on drugs.

The problem of the chronic insomniac, who has been taking sleeping tablets for years and in worrying doses, is totally different. Physiological and psychological addiction, inherent in these drugs, demands a total break from this vicious circle. You must attempt a progressive withdrawal to reduce dependency. Relaxation practices, like meditation, muscular exercises and hydrotherapy, are very useful. Currently, there is a large consensus on two basic therapeutic approaches: on the one hand, the search for a specific cause and treatment, and on the other, the recognition that sleeping remedies must be used with the utmost discretion in chronic insomnia. Treatment should include a diverse range of therapies such as better sleep hygiene and behavioural techniques such as sleep re-education.

People are astounded that champagne can induce sleep as effectively as sleeping pills and without unpleasant side effects. The salutary effect of champagne could be explained by the fact that, in small doses, it stimulates the deep centres of the brain where the release of sleep-inducing substances occurs. Drink too much, and it disrupts these delicate molecules and risks an adverse effect. It cannot, of course, on its own, help the severe insomniacs who are used to a number of drugs. But even in these cases champagne is a useful mediator. As an efficient sleep-inducer it allows the patient to regain confidence and to free himself from anxiety about falling asleep.

Insomnia is more than just a personal headache. It can lead to social and professional problems for people who cannot adapt their daily rhythms to the hours imposed by their working life.

At the beginning of the 18th century a French astronomer, Jean-Jacques d'Ortous de Mairan, made a strange discovery which made him the founder of a new science: chronobiology, which aims to understand the rhythmic functioning of our organs. He had observed that plant growth followed a circadian rhythm. At twilight, for instance, the waning light causes leaves to droop. The growth rate of plants varies from day to night.

A plant placed permanently in darkness will maintain its growth rate for a while. These observations were evidence of a kind of internal clock. In the following centuries more and more precise experiments have shown that all living creatures, from microbes to man, obey the march of time in their physiological functioning.

Perversely, it is at the age when the individual has the most time to sleep that he is deprived of this necessary function and natural pleasure. Insomnia does indeed most often strike the elderly. Sleep disturbance increases with age. Two major reasons lie behind this alteration. Ageing often leads to changes in the wake-sleep rhythm as a consequence of insufficient cerebral irrigation. And, of course, organic and psychological afflictions increase with age.

For example, rheumatic and respiratory disorders and bladder problems can create severe disturbance in the sleep pattern. Anxiety, loneliness and loss of autonomy also contribute to unsettled sleep. A lengthy initial sleep followed by frequent interruptions and a premature awakening lead to the frustrated feeling of having had an awful night. Most elderly people have lost almost all of their deep sleep, reducing their time of rest to no more than three or four hours a night.

For a sleeping remedy to be acceptable it must be easy to manage and non-addictive. It must not cause memory loss or fatigue on awaking, or depress respiration. Its must not lose its efficacy over time. It must act quickly without intoxication or residual side effects. The sleep it brings must be as natural as possible. Unfortunately, an ideal sleeping pill that meets these requirements does not exist.

In general, if you can determine the cause, you are halfway to the cure. Every chronic insomniac needs a full and detailed medical check-up. But the odd bad night requires nothing more than a good dose of common sense and a glass of champagne. One should never take sleeping pills casually, and still less every night.

Even if a glass of champagne were no more effective than a sleeping pill, its side effects will certainly be less damaging. That is why the ancient remedy deserves to be tried by all insomniacs.

'My glass is filled with a wine
flickering like a flame.'
Baudelaire

CHAPTER 10

Depression and Anxiety

The Age of Enlightenment was also the age of *folies vaporeuses*, the vapours. The term encompassed all the miseries of body and mind arising from the unpredictable and indefinable 'erratic humours' which primarily affected young women. The manifestations of this bizarre illness were disparate. Loss of interest, isolation, inappropriate conduct, indifference towards one's friends, self-centredness, irritability, torpor and impulsiveness were amongst the many forms of bizarre behaviour observed during these crises. These vapours or 'humoural miasmas' haunted young girls, their parents and especially the doctors who had to treat them from the 18th century onwards. These mysterious 'vapours', a vague and somewhat poetic term, devastated the body and mind of their victims. This incurable affliction exhibited the most diverse and unexpected symptoms. Suicidal 'calls for help', miraculous cures, uncontrollable laughter and tears were some of its manifestations.

Modern medicine prefers to label these incomprehensible displays 'depression' or a 'depressive state'. Although the terminology is more scientific, it does not really provide a better explanation of the origin of the phenomenon. That is because depression is not a disease but a symptom, like fever or pain, and its causes are manifold.

The complete ignorance of the mechanism of the vapours has allowed for the elaboration of the most fanciful hypotheses. Since the time of 'La Dame aux Camelias', the condition has been attributed to 'erratic character', 'general shrivelling', 'nervous sensitivity', and hypochondria. It has been called the rich man's or the debutante's disease. In the 19th century it was, in fact, fashionable for well-bred young girls of the upper classes to be a little ethereal; it gave them an irresistible romantic charm.

'Most sensual women are vaporous,' pronounced the medical establishment of the period. It was thought at the time that the illness emanated from a sick womb and then invaded the entire organism provoking convulsions, blackouts and hysterics. Naturally, vapours only arose in women. Doctor Raulin, author of the famous treatise 'The Vaporous Affections of the Fairer Sex' (1759), had already raised the alarm: *'The vapours, which have beset the fairer part of the human race since the beginning of medicine...have become more complicated, more delicate, more difficult to cure and more numerous.'*

This description struck terror in our ancestors for three centuries. It is only in our own time that the epidemic has begun to recede thanks to our growing understanding of brain chemistry. Before tranquillisers were invented, one simply

'Plaisir d'amour ne dure qu'un instant;
Chagrin d'amour, dure toute la vie...'

had recourse to the effects of alcohol or wine to chase away the vapours and revive the humours.

It comes as no surprise that the wine of Ay was highly regarded for its delicate and pleasing efficacy, capable of curing hypochondria and re-establishing the balance between the suffering body and the spirit. This remedy, recommended only by experience, proved very useful. Many illustrious men suffering from *'mal de siècle'* or *'mal d'amour'* did not hesitate to turn to this charming and enticing remedy, to this incomparable wine which was able to banish melancholy.

Champagne, elevated to the rank of popular remedy against anguish and sadness, became an instant success with those who sought consolation or oblivion at the bottom of a glass. Poets, artists, lovers across continents and down the centuries have celebrated the enchanting virtues of this inspiring wine. For two centuries, this was how one treated oneself when one sought to soothe anguish or avoid depression. On the whole, it could have been worse. Champagne, bubbling with joy, probably did not cure despondency, but at least it did not have negative side-effects, unlike powerful tranquillisers. We recognise that this ancestral remedy rendered an immense service to generations of men and women who drank in anticipation of comfort and joy.

When psychoanalysis imposed itself, Freud seized upon this business of the vapours. Depression became an illness, a schizoid, if not a schizophrenic, manifestation. It was no longer fashionable to consider it a charm or a whim. Psychoanalysis scrutinised the remotest corners of the subconscious. Practically everything about these depressed states was described, except for the psychopathology which brought them on.

Then one day in 1950, a French naval surgeon, Professor Henri Laborit, discovered the first tranquillizer: chlorpromazine, our Largactil. He demonstrated in the face of initial disbelief that depression was curable chemically, whatever its cause. Neurobiology came into its own. America welcomed Laborit like an infant prodigy, while he remained controversial in his own country.

By then we had been living for half a century under the Freudian dispensation. This unforeseen discovery opened a new area of research. Depression, as well as many other psychic conditions, is often the result of a biochemical disturbance in the brain at the level of complex interactions of messages coming from internal and/or external sources. Depression should thus be looked upon as a simple dysfunction, curable through a combination of drugs and psychotherapy.

Beyond the scientific discovery, the work of Henri Laborit enabled a true psycho-social advance. In showing that the real problem of depression resides in the electro-chemical dialogue between the cells and the circuits of the brain, he swept away the prejudices which the depressed and their families had to struggle against. Unsustainable speculations were rendered obsolete by the immense progress in neurobiology. New discoveries followed; first lithium and then other tranquillizers, each modulating the chemical reactions underlying all mental activity.

The tranquillizer revolution gave rise to two categories of powerful remedies: the neuroleptics or major tranquillizers capable not only of alleviating but also of curing serious psychological problems like paranoia, depressive psychosis, and schizophrenia, and the minor tranquillizers which reduce anxiety, insomnia and distress. Their mode of action is similar to that of wine, owing to the presence of certain calming elements, particularly lithium.

Nothing now escapes the reach of these powerful drugs whose use expands each day. Their profusion is a snare that medicine finds difficult to avoid. Depression, with its manifold changing symptoms, defies rigorous analysis and

'irridescent champagne-suffused with the iconic glow that dispels the darkness'
R.D.

tends to be systematically treated with tranquillizers despite side-effects which can be as disabling as the affliction itself. This therapeutic approach can end up shrinking the infinite dimension of man to its own reductive logic. There is a pill for every bodily misery, every misfortune of the spirit and every foible of civilization. Varied and abundant, but at the same time general and approximate, this chemotherapy for the brain inspires much mistrust and raises many questions. The days are gone when the word 'vapours' was used to describe 'the changing mood, the uneven temper, the pouting, the faces, the affected manners, the simpering which a woman had to permanently put on to be called attractive.' No one is interested in blackouts, diplomatic migraines, palpitations and fake tears except in the theatre.

In the last two decades the science of the nervous system has been at the centre of a revolution silenced by the media noise about the conquest of space. Yet it concerns the greatest conquest man has ever undertaken, that of his own brain. Naturally, these fantastic discoveries, unthinkable only a short time ago, can be used destructively. What do men want to do? Is it better to help the brain or to enslave it? It is obvious that the prolonged use of psychotropic drugs is undesirable. The efficacy of the drugs is not in doubt, but their prescription should be strictly controlled and regulated; their quantity and period of use should be adjusted to the particular circumstances of each individual.

We know that in a normal state the brain secretes calming substances which enable us to cope with the demands of ordinary life. Some therapeutic trials have shown that bouts of depression vary according to whether they originate from excess, shortage or imbalance in one or another of these substances produced by the brain. Champagne can, to some extent, help to regulate these substances, supplement energy, and soothe anxiety because it contains the trace element, lithium.

Curiously, lithium, which is present in the juice of the grape, is not native to our planet. It did not originate in volcanic eruptions or in the cooling of the earth's crust. It comes to us from cosmic space. It originates in the bombardment of interstellar dust by cosmic rays coming from the ends of the universe. Debris containing lithium falls on the earth and oceans. The vine absorbs this element through its roots and traces appear in grape juice and in wine.

We have noted that champagne influences an individual's reactions and it is important to know precisely how what we eat or drink affects our behaviour. We have always had ideas about the connections between what we eat and how we behave. Food has been used as a remedy against anxiety from time immemorial. The ancient Egyptians used onions to help them sleep, almonds and cabbage to counter intoxication, salt to prevent fatigue.

Today, nutritionists and neurophysiologists think that certain foods contain specific substances whose action is like that of neurotransmitters. Once eaten, they contribute to the production of molecules affecting behaviour. Individuals respond more or less well to internal and external attack; some immediately adopt a tactic for resolving their problem, others respond with anxiety, prolonging their distress and further disturbing their behaviour. These are usually the ones who have recourse to tranquillizers and who run the risk of succumbing to addiction through prolonged use. Many could lift their mood just as well with a small flute of cold wine.

Disorders stemming from depression can now be cured thanks to new anti-depressive drugs. Because of its multiplicity of causes and manifestations, and the complexity of its biological genesis, it is obvious that there cannot be a single standard treatment adapted to all forms of depression. We are now in the third millennium, but the vapours are still with us under different names. They are filling the waiting rooms of doctors. Despite fantastic technological breakthroughs we have not yet been able to fully understand the interplay of body and mind which sadly continues to defy medical progress.

'God did not want the noble wine to waste;
that is why, He not only gave us the vine,
but also the noble thirst.'
Winzerspruch of Dorlisheim

CHAPTER 11

Drugs and Intoxication

Every year the French consume fifty-six million boxes of sleeping pills and seventy million boxes of sedatives. The whole market for sedatives, tranquillizers, barbiturates and benzodiazepine pills amounts to over several billion francs. The French are unfortunately tranquillizer addicts. Over three billion doses are consumed every year! That is five times more per capita than in the United States.

Tranquillizers are psychotropic substances created by our stressful civilization to suppress the neurotic anguish of our times. The benzodiazepine family is mostly used for that purpose. If these figures are rarely published it is because the large drug companies do not wish to be the only ones held responsible for the mass consumption of products often advised against by medical associations. The prime culprit is, of course, the consumer himself who prefers taking a miracle pill to confronting the underlying reasons for his anguish.

That these drugs are effective in the treatment of psychic and emotional distress is undeniable. But how can one explain the fact that benzodiazepines are the most commonly used drugs in France? For example, more than a billion pills of Temesta are sold every year. This star of our pharmacopoeia has transformed the French into the most chemically sedated people in the world. This fabulous market is shared among thirty suppliers. The sedative mass market is not only an economic fact, it is the hallmark of our civilisation. It indicates a collective adherence to a certain mode of resolving our problems, a quest for and focus on instant results, and at a deeper level, a new morality.

This new collective intoxication is perhaps not as threatening technically as illegal hard drugs, but this abuse is not entirely without danger. A recent survey showed that women have recourse to repeated use of these products more than men. This arises partly from the characteristics of their sleep. The quality of women's nocturnal repose is inferior to that of men.

Consumption patterns of sleeping pills and tranquillizers vary amongst the regions. The greatest use is in the Paris region while Alsace and Champagne have the lowest incidence, 11 per cent less than the national average. It is interesting that the most economically depressed regions seem to find other means of calming their anxiety than these medications. How can one explain the dreadful success of tranquillisers in a country where the children of Asterix are best known for their liveliness and *joie de vivre?*

Benzodiazepines have primarily a tranquillizing action. They erase fear as if by magic. They loosen defence mechanisms while provoking drowsiness. Their effect on the brain is to lower vigilance and psychomotor activity. Moreover, they can magnify the effect of other drugs such as tobacco, alcohol and other sedatives. Their mode of action remains unclear.

Anxiety, far from being our worst enemy, is in fact a most useful defence mechanism. It modifies the functioning of organs controlled by the peripheral nervous system. When we are anxious, the cardiac and pulmonary rhythms accelerate; blood flows more rapidly and swells the muscles. The adrenal glands receive the danger signal from the brain and declare a state of alert by pumping adrenalin: the hormone which enables the organism to respond to external aggression. This internal commotion serves a function of vital importance in that anxiety, the engine of creativity, is necessary to man. It enabled our prehistoric ancestors to generate the surplus energy required to fight ferocious predators, or at least to gather their strength to flee.

The different drugs do not behave in the same way in the circulatory system. The most tenacious exhibit a curious trait: destroyed and transformed in the liver cells they become new benzodiazepines which continue to work on the brain after the initial effect is over. Their damage is thus prolonged in the organism and adds cumulatively to the effect of any new pills the subject takes.

Depending on the speed with which they dissolve in fat, some molecules penetrate the control barrier of the brain more easily. Halcion requires half an hour, but Seresta needs two to four hours. Elimination of these substances depends on the condition of the liver. Anything which slows the functioning of the liver cells automatically leads to an accumulation of toxins. Moreover, the partial retention of toxins also

Miss Mercier

'Nothing equals the joy of the drinker, like the joy of the wine being drunk.'
Anon

Edward VII in Paris

'Pleasure without champagne is purely artificial.'
Oscar Wilde

impedes the destruction of other organic waste. We shall see later on how the organism can avoid this intoxication.

When champagne is consumed in small doses it stimulates the activity of the liver cells and increases the effectiveness of the purifying enzymes. This works as long as the wine is drunk in moderation. The foolhardy person who drinks too much can easily reach the reverse condition. Excess provokes panic amongst the enzymes, cleansing stops and the surplus wine attacks the cell instead of helping it. Those are the paradoxical effects of champagne that one should keep in mind if one wants to exploit its purifying properties.

Astonishingly, the organism of some individuals is able to adapt itself progressively when the consumption of toxins is prolonged and the dose is high. The liver reacts by producing a surplus of enzymes to neutralise the poison. As a result a biological balance is achieved, leaving the liver unharmed.

In small quantities the energy and the additional ions of champagne help to activate enzymatic activity. As the enzymes do not act simultaneously, some can hunt down toxins while others remain in reserve to be called into action later. It is likely that under the stimulation of the wine, all the enzymes mobilise at the same time to eliminate undesirable substances.

Albumin is our first line of defence against toxic molecules. It traps most of them as soon as they penetrate into the bloodstream. Champagne enriches the ions in the bloodstream, activating a state of electrostatic attraction in the albumin with detoxifying effect. But it is not just the enzymes and albumin which are charged with defending us against poisoning. Each cell is equipped with special pumps whose function is to ensnare and eject from the cell any toxic substance. Along the intestinal wall, as well as inside the arteries and veins, these pumps eliminate most of the toxins which invade the cell. Thus there are security devices at all levels but their work demands considerable expense of energy. It can be enhanced if one knows how to encourage them with the appropriate energy booster.

It is clear that the substances furnished by champagne contribute to the rapid activation of the purification process. This is because champagne works by natural means, both delicate and effective. However, there is always the risk of paralysing the process by any excess. A superabundance of energy will unfailingly upset the subtle equilibrium of this physiological mechanism which exists in all animals to protect them from attack by chemical substances in their environment. We must always treat champagne as a remedy rather than as a drink.

Tradition has always exploited this regulatory property of champagne. Tsar Peter the Great, who suffered from the ill-effects of tobacco and spirits, came to appreciate the cleansing quality of champagne while travelling in France. The King of Spain, Philip V, drank champagne to calm his agitated nights. Many famous writers – Pushkin, Goethe, Byron, Claudel, Camus – found solace in this euphoric sparkling wine, just like all those *'most honest people who each night filled themselves with champagne, as with a propitious gas, to see them through the night.'* (Hoffman)

'Since I love you so much,
I must kiss you;
You must, luscious wine,
kiss me too.'
J. Le Houx

CHAPTER 12

Gynecological Troubles

The kings, who made France, have all attempted to perpetuate their dynasty by increasing their chances of producing a male heir. No surprise then that champagne was highly valued both as nourishment and as a refined remedy to give the procreators a better chance of attaining their objective. It also calmed the nausea of early pregnancy in their consorts.

The choice of a fertile spouse of noble lineage; the obstetric care of midwives and doctors; the highly ritualised reception ceremony for the newborn; the role devolved to Church dignitaries; the celebrations given to the populace when the child was male: these tell us more about the character of the reigning royals than any history subject to partisan interpretation.

The queens of France were placed in the hands of reputable midwives, in France called 'wise-women' whose credentials had to be approved by the court surgeon and by the pre-eminent notable of the parish, the curate. During pregnancy the Queen's diet had to be especially rich and varied with first-rate wines, which were also consumed after delivery to irrigate and cleanse the womb. The food intended to quickly restore the mother's health was carefully balanced. It was especially important if she had given birth to a girl, as the mother had to be promptly readied for a new pregnancy in the hope of doing better next time and producing the anticipated boy. Although doctors did not participate in the delivery, they oversaw the proceedings from a suitable distance and fussed about the thousand precautions to be taken in the pre- and post-delivery diet. It was during the delivery of the bastards of Madame de Montespan, the Sun King's mistress *officielle*, that doctors first became involved. She was prescribed a pint of semi-dry champagne with each meal during pregnancy to strengthen the foetus, and a double dose after delivery to hasten recovery.

In a country of Salic Law, which excludes females from the succession, the rage of kings, princes, and even cardinals *('o tempora, o mores!')* to produce male descendants was admirable, a sort of frantic, heroic pursuit. '*One has seen men who spared nothing to produce offspring, especially of the noble sex. The art which teaches this secret could not be more highly esteemed, as from it arises the happiness of States and the tranquility of families.*' Nicholas Venette's remark is good evidence of the mentality reigning at the end of the 17th century. On the contrary, this fierce determination to beget a male heir would push misogyny to a climax in centuries to come.

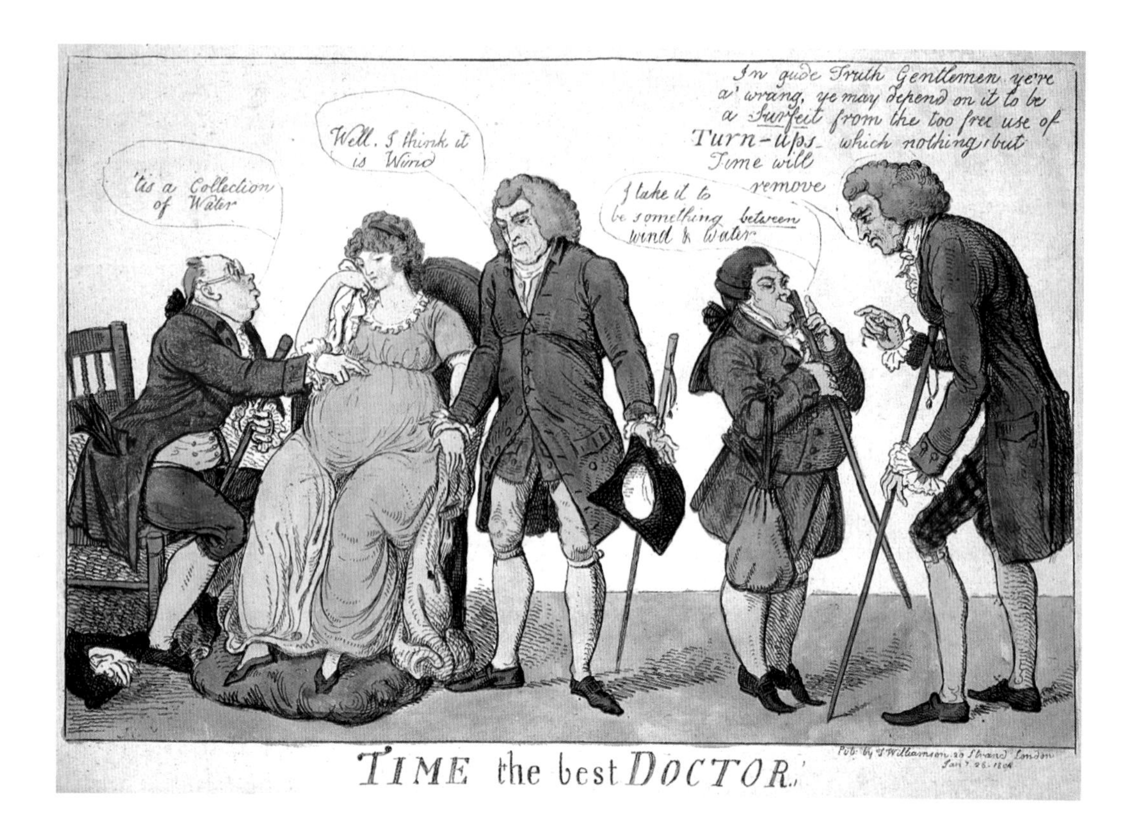

It was not really a new idea, nor was it specifically French. This pride in producing only males is common to all times and places. So one should not be astonished at the proliferation of a highly specialised 'how-to' literature which, over three centuries, has developed and refined various recipes aiming to teach couples 'The Art of Producing Boys'. Until the middle of the 19th century our ancestors still firmly believed that 'each procreation adhering to the rules of the art would produce only males.' Females were considered the result of some imperfection, of a clumsiness that some simple precaution could have avoided.

It is in this context that male-producing diets were developed. To begin with the couple should drink white wines only. Those of Burgundy and Champagne were of course the noblest and most sought after for their virile potency. Certain recipes advised powdered womb of hare. The white testicles of billy goats were highly prized, as male engenders male. But woe to those who consumed one only! They ran the risk of producing a mono-testicled son!

The coupling itself, after a long and detailed preparation, had to proceed in joy, as sadness resulted only in girls. That, of course, required the consumption of first class wines to jollify the creative humours! The frolics could then proceed in a warm bed scented with musk.

Yet, despite these elaborate precautions, the number of girls, strangely enough, always remained the same! Experts came up with a new high-tech method. This combined anatomic and balletic approach, postulated that each testicle was responsible for one sex; the right one, naturally, for boys. The man had thus to tilt leftwards and aim at the right ovary of his spouse which captured the male seed. The angle of the 'canon of life' was aimed with precision thanks to the effects of wine judiciously consumed before the act. At the crucial moment the left hand of the husband had to slide briskly under the hip of his consort and lift her quickly to an angle of 30 degrees relative to his fertilising axis. As one can see, begetting a male required a technique of infinite delicacy and complexity. The artillery was at a distinct advantage. We must give full credit to our ancestors for their single-minded and acrobatic endeavours.

Even if this operation was successful, that was not the end of the story. If the newborn boy looked weak or did not cry he was sometimes immersed in a fortifying wine concoction. It even happened that he was made to drink a mouthful: 'Many midwives fill their mouth with wine which they gently blow into the child's as soon as he emerges,' notes one obstetrician. This was common practice in Champagne.

History relates that Louis XIV managed to escape this old-fashioned kiss of life. When born the French prince was first bathed in lukewarm lustral water. He was then placed on a silver platter to be clothed in the shirt sent by Pope UrbanVIII and then wrapped in swaddling clothes also blessed by the Holy Father, to show that he was recognised as the eldest son of the Church. Governesses, sub-governesses, wet nurses and rockers surrounded the young Dauphin. The doctor and pharmacist attached to the Dauphin's household kept a close watch over the diet of the wet nurse who had to eat quantities of meat and consume noble wine to enrich her milk. History does not report whether this special tasting milk, which he had to suckle twice a night until the age of ten months, was to his liking. But it may have become

We are not amused

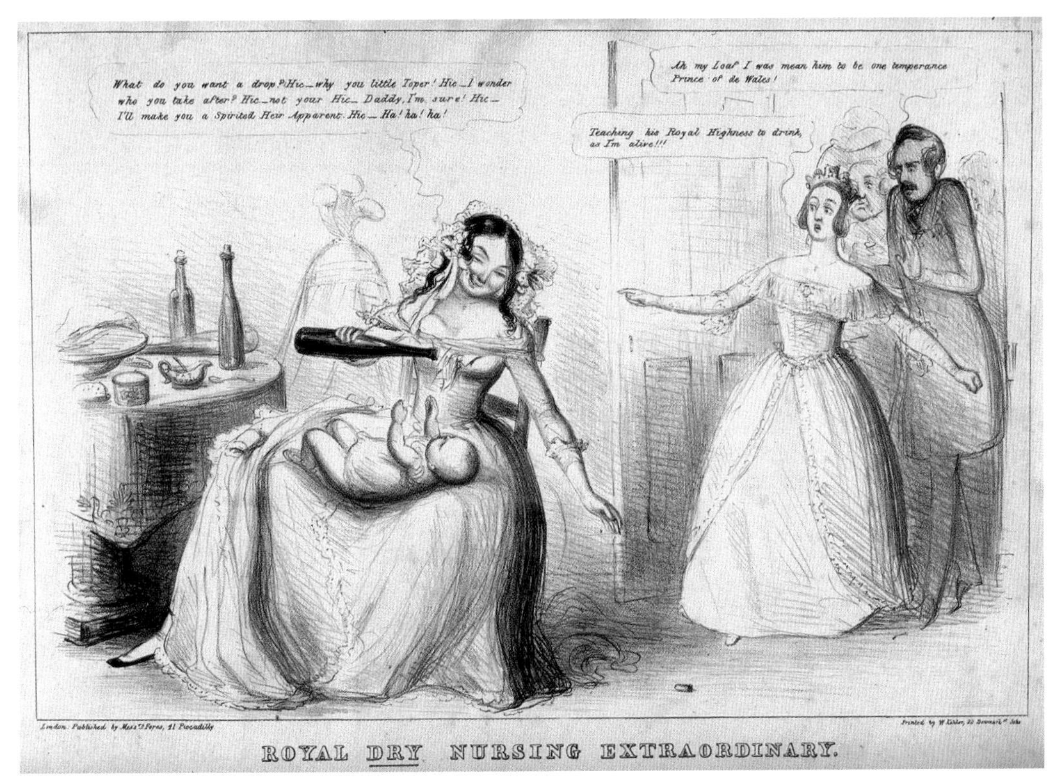

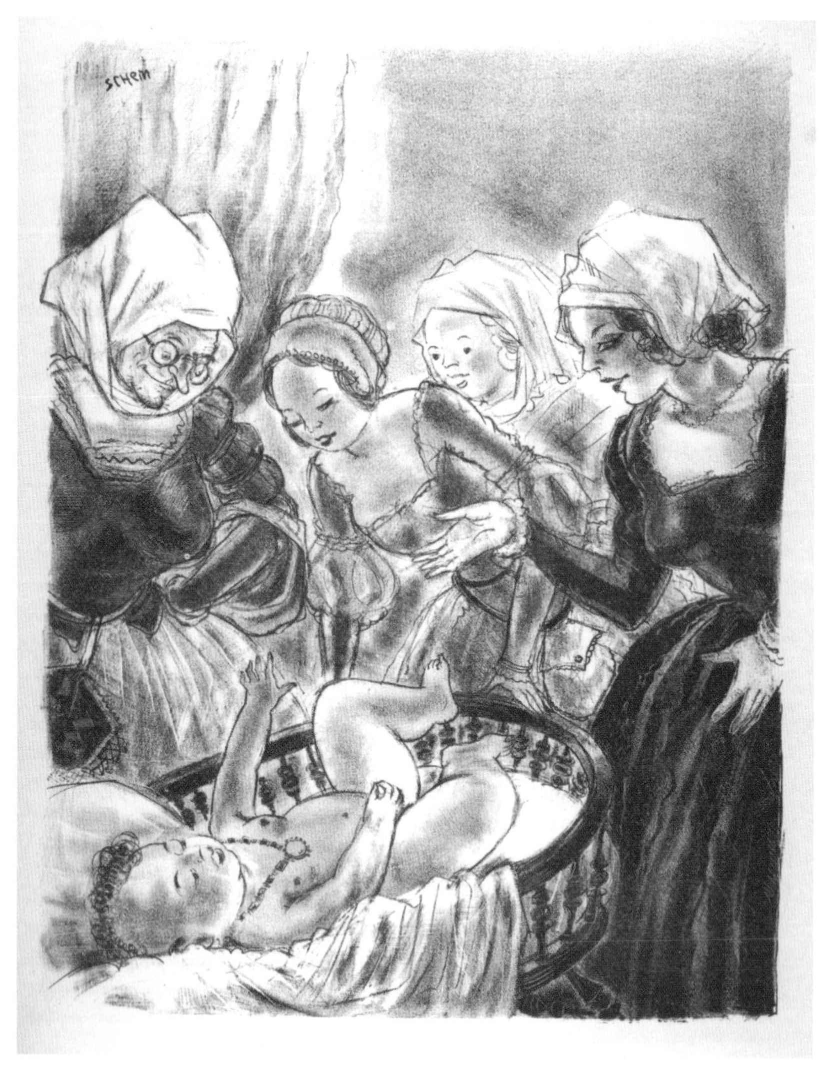

It's a boy!

an acquired taste: during the whole of his life he drank only the best wine of Champagne, at least until 1695 when his doctor, alarmed at the state of the august stomach, made him switch to old burgundies as they are less acid.

This tradition is another mark of the secular prestige of champagne, renowned for its tonic qualities, which are particularly salutary before and after delivery and while breast-feeding. From the 18th century onwards, this ancestral remedy was systematically prescribed to help women through the awesome trial of childbirth.

The fascinating nature of women and the enduring idea that their sex was the source of all evils help to explain the multitude of symptoms loosely grouped under the term 'feminine affliction', which kept the doctors of the bourgoisie busy and in silk.

The most precocious of these feminine afflictions was chlorosis or green sickness, an epidemic which struck only young girls. Their strange pallor and tender fragility haunted the popular imagination. Immortal heroines, they peopled the pages of novels as much as medical observations. The temptation of 'angelism', the exaltation of youth, the delicacy of virginity, kept alive the myth of the lily-white young girl whose very complexion combined radiance and wasting away.

Chlorosis became the enigmatic malady to which sentimental young girls of good family succumbed, and which disappeared as if by magic after the long awaited salutary marriage. The prolixity of the medical discourse on this topic by the mid-nineteenth century is enlightening and went far beyond what was accepted earlier. Dysfunction of the menstrual cycle, involuntary manifestation of sexual awakening, stomach spasm, hereditary or family disease, madness or pubescent hysteria are some of the theories put forward in profusion by novelists and doctors. Even today one cannot but be touched by the moving struggle of heroines fighting the metamorphosis of their bodies and hearts. Victor Hugo described their pathetic charm: *'She had this fleeting grace of deportment, which signals this most delicate of transitions, adolescence, the two twilights confused, the dawn of a woman and the end of a child.'*

Without a doubt fantasies attached to the menstrual blood could not fail to contribute to the idea of the feminine condition. Worried parents feverishly arranged a marriage, their only hope of passing through this difficult time. Meanwhile, young girls were prescribed lukewarm food (hot food would fan the flames of desire) and champagne, whose virtue was beyond doubt. Many of them were, in effect, miraculously cured by the vivifying wine, or perhaps by the prospect of marriage.

Finally, towards the end of the century, a discovery shed light on this most mysterious symptom. Chlorosis was simply due to iron deficiency, which caused the extreme pallor of these adorable creatures.

Progress in understanding the causes of anaemia and the practice of globular numeration fully vindicated the traditional champagne treatment since champagne is rich in ferric ions. One flute per meal, the equivalent of 0.4mg of iron, is largely sufficient to cover daily requirements. This prescription, which is far superior to the previous arsenic-based tonics, progressively reduces pallor. Champagne is also recommended in the case of painful periods as its calcium and potassium ions relieve and calm undesirable symptoms.

From the earliest times the menstrual flux has inspired fascination and profound wonder about the mystery of life. All civilisations have attempted, through their rituals, to master the power of these rhythmic manifestations, ruled by the lunar cycle. They especially feared the impurity associated with the menses. To purify oneself became a constant cultural and religious obsession. All sorts of irrational practices from the isolation of women during their periods to washing with water, salt, and plant brews, and the incantation of magic formulas were adopted to preserve men from this physiological pollution. People also periodically practised rebirthing rites to free themselves from everything which had been in contact with the impure.

Sometimes, however, the stain was transformed into purity. Women in the Bible are associated with the powerful tree of life archetype. The 'Song of Songs' praises their fertility by comparing them to the vine:

'Your mother was like a vine plant
She was fecund and leafy,
She grew powerful stocks
Which became royal sceptres.'

In man's consciousness the feminine mystery tends to dominate over all. Few divinities have had the right and power to reign over both the sacred and the profane, the light and the shadow. This ascension of woman to the realm of supreme forces finds its origin in man's fascination with maternity and menstruation. Even now, there are traces of those times when she was in turn worshipped and vilified. Women were long forbidden to come near the wine press during menstruation. Until the Renaissance, women were forbidden to enter church during their periods. The despicable men who had relations with them at that time were subject to the same taboo. They had to atone for their sin by fasting on bread and wine, the only food that could cleanse the stain. There are still remnants of the irrational fear which held that everything coming from the female body was capable of sullying or bewitching her frail partner. But over the centuries women have never lost the archaic privileges of 'Mistress of the Hearth', source of warmth in which one buries the dead so they can be reborn.

How many women do suffer from their menstruation? Surveys in Europe as well as in the United States, show that 40 per cent complain and that 10 per cent are more or less handicapped either just before or during the first two days of their period. Nearly all women are affected at least once in their lives, though the intensity of the discomfort varies from one person and one age to another. It is true that the contraceptive pill, when properly prescribed, helps alleviate period pain quite remarkably. If the worst cases require a full medical examination, most are relatively benign without organic or functional causes. The recommendation then is to lead a more active life, consume less coffee and cola (which contains xanthines which disturb the hormonal regulatory circuits), and take more magnesium, calcium and vitamins B and B6. We know that champagne contains a quantity of these substances, which again places it on the list of traditional, sovereign remedies.

Sometimes, the abundance of menses is due to the administration of inappropriate hormones (mostly oestrogen). Some categories of pill can trigger these problems. The tonic effect of champagne can soothe and hasten recovery while waiting for a medical diagnosis and the prescription of another type of pill.

It is natural that champagne, as part of the family daily pharmacopoeia, should be closely linked with the early treatment of period troubles. However, the initial period of pregnancy is critical and it is then most advisable to abstain from any type of alcohol whatsoever. After delivery, on the other hand, it is quite salutary and in line with custom, to have the tired mother partake of a glass of champagne to boost her general condition. Such is the paradox of this wine that its virtues depend on circumstances. Knowing that quantity is not synonymous with quality one should treat this beverage with great respect and moderation in order to optimise the potency of its healing power.

'There comes a time in every womans's life when the only thing that helps is a glass of champagne.'
Bette Davis

CHAPTER 13

Gerontology

King Gilgamesh, who reigned over Uruk on the left bank of the Euphrates, vanquished the giant Humaba after a titanesque struggle. He then became the favourite of the goddess Inanna. Our hero was not content with the mere beauty of the divinity. He also wanted to discover the secret of immortality. He succeeded in obtaining the secret in the form of a magic plant. But somehow distracted, he let it be stolen by a serpent. Ever since, his descendants have had to resign themselves to their mortality. Man has been rebelling for five thousand years against the gods' monopoly on immortality. The twenty five thousand clay tablets discovered by archaeologists in the library of King Ashurbanipal in Ninevah tell the moving epic of Gilgamesh who searched in vain for a remedy for age and death. A similar fate befell humanity's first couple, Adam and Eve, cast out of Eden for daring to taste the fruit of the Tree of Life. In these myths, gods have condemned humans to an inevitable death while they go on forever. Clearly, to live a long and healthy life has always been humanity's dream.

Tithon of Troy, brother of Priam, was also lucky enough to marry a goddess, Eos, the divinity of dawn, who fell in love with the beauty and strength of the young prince. Overcome by love she asked Zeus to grant her husband eternal life, but foolishly forgot to ask him for eternal youth. So poor Tithon was condemned to age eternally, reduced to a pitiable senility. Deprived of all earthly pleasures he could only lament, in his long solitude, that others would, in the end, find the final rest which would always elude him.

Men seemed condemned never to acquire immortality. After a quarrel, Zeus punished Prometheus, the creator of the human race, by withdrawing fire from men. Prometheus raided the Olympus, stole the fire and returned it to man. In revenge, Zeus ordered Hephaestus to create a woman and blow the four winds into her to bring her to life. This woman, Pandora, as beautiful as she was stupid, malicious and lazy, opened the jar in which Prometheus had locked away all the evils which afflict humankind, including old age, disease and death. All the calamities jumped out of the jar and have beset mankind ever since.

But it takes more than that to discourage the human race in its quest for longevity. From Aristotle to Descartes, through Epicurus and Lucretius, their single-minded dedication to the pursuit of the dream has been admirable.

In the depths of the woods of Mount Olympus, Zeus transformed the nymph Juventas into a fountain of youth. Her waters gave off the most exquisite fragrance and whoever was fortunate enough to bathe in them was immediately restored to youth and health. When the Spaniards discovered the New World they thought they would find the mythic fountain there. Ponce de León, a Spanish navigator, undertook an expedition to retrieve its miraculous waters for the King of Spain. One morning in 1513, his ships reached a paradisiacal isle. It was Florida; but the famous fountain was not there. Ponce de León was badly deceived. He died some years later, struck by an Indian's poisoned arrow as he explored the jungle.

Ever since and everywhere, biologists and gerontologists have tirelessly pursued this work. They discovered that the mythical water was not hidden in some enchanted wood but in the invisible nucleus of our cells. What they found is both marvellous and hopeless: death and life are inscribed in it. All is recorded and fixed in the book of life: the miniscule fragment of desoxyribonucleic acid, DNA, coiled in the double helix.

In fact, human longevity has not really increased in a significant manner over the millennia and the Biblical 'three-score year and ten' remains the norm. What has happened is that average life-expectancy has increased thanks to improvements in living conditions and medical progress. If the major causes of death were eliminated, longevity would still only extend to one hundred years. From a certain age, disorders associated with natural degeneration begin to appear which gradually wear down the arteries, the immune system, and the faculty of repair. The organism becomes increasingly vulnerable in the elderly years of age. Researchers believe the decline of the human body starts around thirty, and that after this transitional age, our functional capacities decrease at a rate of 2 per cent a year.

In reality, our cells renew themselves while keeping up the apparent unity of the body. Except for the nerve and muscle cells, all constituents of our organism change continuously. The billions of molecules and atoms composing our structure undergo constant repair. The enzymes correct defective functioning, take away worn parts, replace them, put them back to work, and coordinate their activities at an incredible pace. Viewed from this angle, the body, despite its unchanging appearance, is like a flowing river, never quite the same, yet never entirely different. This ongoing renewal, however, has its limits, which in effect define the ageing phenomenon.

Biologists, trying to prove that the possible number of cell divisions is inscribed in our genes, have succeeded in replacing the nucleus of a young cell with an old one. The cell was unable to divide further and died. They have also rejuvenated an old cell with a nucleus taken from a young cell. These experiments show that the internal clock, which regulates cell division, is located in the nucleus. We even know that this faculty is inscribed in the sixth chromosome pair where the immune defence programme and our biological identity are also stored. No surprise then that longevity varies from individual to individual, as does immune resistance to various diseases. We also know that certain specialised cells (brain cells, muscle cells, glands) do not subdivide and are thus irreplaceable, although their molecular structure itself is subject to permanent renewal. It is these very cells which are the most fragile and most subject to alterations with age. In the elderly, these cells speed up chemical changes in the use of nutritive substances; in the expression and repair of genetic material; in the functioning of the cellular machinery; in the efficiency of enzymes; in the morphology of membranes; and in the elements which compose them. In short, the old cell slowly wears out and is extinguished.

Z. Medvedev of the Medical Research Council proposed the first explanation of the mechanism responsible for the alterations in the living cell. According to his theory, the organism is bound to make mistakes in the course of years of functioning.

Normally these chemical errors are corrected by specialised enzymes, which maintain a normal level of efficient functionality. However, following excesses (tobacco, alcohol, sunburn, poor diet, lack of exercise), the enzymes lose their efficiency and allow errors to accumulate in the cells. These cumulative errors lead to the production of defective, even suicidal, hormones and enzymes which marks the beginning of the decline of the cell. If only one cell is involved, the problem is easily resolved: the cell is simply eliminated and replaced. But when the mistakes overtake a whole system, nervous, circulatory or immune, then degenerative diseases will unfailingly threaten life. It is possible to partly remedy the situation by adopting a healthier life style, and by absorbing the vitamins and trace elements required by the enzymes to boost their ability to repair; especially to repair the DNA of the nucleus. Fortunately, human cells have an extraordinary capacity to regenerate themselves. This faculty is proportionate to the longevity of the species. Human life is about twice as long as that of a chimpanzee and the ability to correct DNA damage is twice as high. One could compare these processes to what happens to a car. The engineers define an 'average life expectancy' during which the car should (theoretically) run without problems. The day mechanical faults start appearing, it is possible to prolong its life with judicious repairs, as long as spare parts are available. But the machine cannot last forever and without repairs or spares, will eventually be scrapped.

From this point of view, it seems that the ageing mechanism is already programmed in our genes and that our way of life only intervenes to accelerate or slow the life clock. The skin is the best example: it ages prematurely when exposed to excessive sun. One must keep in mind that it is old age, and not youth, which is ageless. Psychologically and physiologically, old age can set in at any moment of life. So the battle is not against old age in itself, but against all the factors which make us age before our time!

Ageing and death are our common fate. However, there are two kinds of cells which escape the common fate: cancer cells and sexual cells (spermatozoids and ova) because what really matters for life is first and foremost the survival of the species and not of individuals. It seems that the sexual cells use the death of other cells in a Machiavellian fashion to ensure their own survival and that is why unlocking their secret may help us prolong longevity. Molecular biology has started to reveal part of their mystery. It seems that their incredible faculty to escape ageing lies essentially in the field of information transmission. They can, in effect, recombine their genes, wind back the fatal clock, reshuffle the cards and redistribute information to inhibit, accelerate, slow down or block, and thanks to this strategy avoid all traps set by the course of time. The great paradox: their carrier is destined to die for the immortality of the species. This concept of life and death guides research into means by which cells communicate and accept or refuse messages. It may be that we will find answers to these questions in the ways in which cells exchange information. The ability to decode their messages and their silence may one day allow us to improve the repair capacity of our enzymes and reduce errors occurring during the transmission of programmes.

Researchers now think they can find the elixir of youth in the youthful power of the sexual cells, since they seem to be the only ones capable of slowing down the inexorable march of time, by freezing some of their genes, and even temporarily interrupting all communication in order to stop the clock.

Wisdom steeped in tradition has always recommended that elderly people drink

Ages beautifully

a flute of champagne with each meal to fortify themselves, as champagne contributes an appreciable boost of energy. One frequently observes in elderly subjects inexplicable cases of malnutrition, while their diet is apparently satisfactory. This deficiency occurs not only because of poor dentition (dental prostheses, even good ones, only provide 30 per cent of the normal mastication efficiency) but also because of a decrease in secretion of saliva with its enzymatic content, and a further 25 per cent drop in gastric secretion. It is mainly at the level of the intestine that senescence leads to major degradation. The intestine wall thins, the villous carpet which covers the inside of the digestive tract atrophies, while the follicular layer also thins. As troubles never come singly, the secretion of the intestinal and pancreatic glands also changes. The digestive hormones and enzymes no longer perform their regulatory role and the intestinal flora run rampant. The elderly subject frequently has a delicate digestion and suffers from the slightest deviation in his ordinary diet. He has difficulty assimilating proteins and fats and tends to eat more sugar. The anatomical and functional changes in the digestive tract often lead to intestinal transit problems (constipation, diarrhoea, bloating). Food absorption, already deficient, becomes even more difficult and impacts on the other vital systems, such as the muscles, bony tissues and circulatory system. A vicious circle takes hold.

Yet many elderly people have good appetites as long as they maintain the quality of their diet, especially foods that provide energy to reinforce and encourage the cellular machinery. This is essential when threatened by cold or stress, during periods of convalescence or loss of appetite. If the elderly tolerate excessive fats and sugar less well, they also require more vitamins, more minerals and biological substances of good quality.

Popular medicine frequently recommends champagne in these circumstances. Faithful to its mission, champagne is always ready to lend a helping hand, and experience shows its usefulness, not as some mythical elixir but as a healthy beverage, biologically and nutritionally. In moderation, this tonic wine seems to give new vigour to the worn out organism. To one's surprise the weakened body little by little regains its strength, its dynamism, its appetite, its taste for life. That is why it is customary to offer a little fortifying wine to a feeble person, while continuing the prescribed medical treatment.

On this topic, one should remember that certain illnesses and certain remedies, diuretics amongst others, induce intestinal problems. People who are confined to bed for long periods, or who suffer joint pains, often lose their appetite. Fever, diuretics, or poor functioning of the centres regulating thirst can cause dehydration. These are all connected and between them weaken the immune defence mechanism, the nervous system and most importantly the capacity to eliminate waste products. These accumulate slowly and when the organism reveals itself incapable of neutralising them, the ageing process takes a leap forward.

Analysis of the faecal matter of the elderly often shows defective digestion of proteins, unbalanced consumption of fats and carbohydrates as well as of vitamins and minerals. This explains why champagne is so highly regarded. Its calcium, phosphorus, magnesium, iron, zinc, copper, manganese, sugars and other vitamin contents are ideally suited to the basic requirements of a frail organism.

We are far from penetrating the secrets of the benefits of champagne for the elderly. Recent work reveals that even water molecules present in champagne acquire

Champagne Monarchists

'Gentlemen, in the little moment that remains to us between the crisis and the catastrophe, we may as well drink a glass of champagne.'
Paul Claudel

an ionic charge, which endows them with exceptional biological properties. This is what biochemists call the hydrogen link, a connection whose fundamental role remains unknown.

'It is true that one cannot find the philosopher's stone, but it is good to keep searching: while searching one stumbles across many a secret one was not looking for.'

It was Fontenelle who dared this quest for the ideal. At ninety-five he confided that the secret of his longevity and good health lay in drinking a little champagne every day. He died a centenarian with his wits intact. To the frivolous Marquise who enquired: 'How goes it, Monsieur de Fontenelle?' he replied, in his last breath, 'It goes, it goes, Marquise, and then it's gone!'

The ageing process is apparently immutable, and yet little by little our understanding of the secret life of the cells grows. Man, fired by this great passion for life, strives to maintain and prolong vital energy, the hallmark of youth. Is champagne an elixir of youth? Yes, if you believe Regnard:

'Yes indeed, champagne again, until there is no more.
You can count every tooth in my mouth
And yet I'm ninety-four!'

'We are all in the gutter, but some of us (and none more so than Dom Perignon) are looking at the stars.'
with excuses to Oscar Wilde

CHAPTER 14

Food Allergies

There is no doubt that allergic reactions occur in the digestive tract. Our digestive apparatus is equipped with a highly sophisticated immune system which plays a prime role in confronting the legion of foreign substances we ingest daily.

All along the intestinal wall we find Peyer's Patches: aggregates of lymphoid tissues not unlike those in the tonsils, charged with the protection of our biological integrity. These lymphocytes reach up to the superficial layers of the digestive mucous membrane where they function to produce antibodies of all sorts: liver enzymes, and benign stomach, pancreatic and intestinal bacteria operate to neutralise undesirable bacteria. But that is still not enough. The internal face of the digestive tract, the mucous membrane, is further endowed with the specialised Langerhans cells. All tissue in contact with the external environment: the skin, the membrane of the digestive tract, the bronchia, the urinary and genital tracts, is permanently under surveillance by these tireless policemen known as the islets of Langerhans in honour of the German doctor who first discovered them.

The Langerhans cells are the front line sentinels of our immune defence system. The digestive membrane is permanently exposed to multiple attacks from chemical, physical, viral and microbial agents. Detection of these harmful invaders rests on these highly specialised cells.

Not everyone presents the same susceptibility to external attack on the digestive system. It is likely that several factors play a part: individual pre-disposition, the nature of the food consumed, the conditions in which it was prepared, interference from other substances absorbed, these are among the many causes which may provoke an allergic reaction. The Langerhans cells hidden on the surface of the digestive cavity can sometimes react in an exacerbated and incoherent fashion. This could explain the hypersensitivity of certain individuals. The prevalence of this particular immune defence system means that any foreign substance is aggressively attacked. As a consequence, unusual reactions occur when this system does not function harmoniously. There are many tendencies which could be the source of allergies. If one wants to determine an efficient treatment for allergies one must try to understand the origin of this often inexplicable phenomenon.

There are many studies attempting to assign responsibility for food allergies to specific foods. According to surveys, about 12 per cent of patients can identify the food they cannot tolerate. Some people cannot allow themselves the slightest dietary latitude while others can eat the incriminated food without any consequences. To better understand these abnormalities the first step is to analyse the chemical make-up of the offending food. The prime suspects are the artificial sweeteners, colouring agents, additives, preserving agents, anti-oxidants. For example, alginate, a gelling agent used in pastry and charcuterie, is an extract from a seaweed containing iodine which could provoke a reaction in some subjects. Citric acid, a preservative added to fruit juices and tinned vegetables, can irritate the gastric mucous membrane because of its acidity, although strictly speaking this would not be classified as an allergic reaction. Glutamate, present in frozen dishes, is regarded as a taste enhancer. Although it does not necessarily affect the stomach it does inhibit the activity of the gastro-intestinal enzymes when too abundant. We do not yet know whether it is toxic to the liver and pancreas. There is a long list of additives about whose side effects we know nothing.

Fruit and vegetable intolerances have been known for a long time. Pollens are the probable cause. Amongst vegetables causing allergies, the umbellifers – angelica, aniseed, carrot, celery, chervil, coriander, cumin, fennel, and to a lesser extent the solanaceous family – potatoes, peppers, tomatoes- are the best known. In general, several allergies coexist, for instance, those due to melon, bananas and fragrant plants or those triggered simultaneously by celery and birch.

For reasons yet to be explained, women are more often the victims of allergic reactions. If they are on the pill, the contraceptive hormone can sometimes exacerbate the symptoms. In the end it is difficult to say whether it is a hormonal or a nutritional allergy. One must also be aware that many pharmaceutical drugs (iron sulphate, aspirin, anti-inflammatories) can also upset the stomach and make it more susceptible to this or that type of food. If taken on an empty stomach they can heighten sensitivity.

All these manifestations may well stem from an irritation of the mucous membrane. If it is provoked by incompatible foods, it may be possible to set up a preventive diet that works in the case of specific and identified products. Unfortunately, in many cases the list of suspect food becomes so long that daily life could become very monotonous and frustrating, without necessarily staving off allergic reaction. Diets pompously labelled '*oligo-antigenic*' are rarely pursued for long because they are too severe and unappetising. The best one can do is to advise patients to carefully monitor what they eat and observe what foods trigger reactions. Once such foods are identified one has to abstain from them for several months. If the digestive manifestations still persist, then they can be eliminated from the list of possible causes. Then one must switch to a broader-based treatment aimed at the whole person.

The juice of the grape is especially rich in magnesium, as well as traces of cobalt and other mineral salts which endows champagne with unsuspected powers to regulate our immune defences against allergic attacks. By a fortunate coincidence champagne is also fairly rich in sulphur. This substance, like magnesium, is a polyvalent anti-allergen. Their association explains the desensitising noted in food intolerance. In practical terms, a monthly treatment of a flute of champagne, after a meal, forestalls and calms digestive troubles.

Of course, it is strongly recommended to abstain from wine in the case of stomach pain, as a hidden ulcer might well be lurking in the shadows. In such a situation it is most important to diagnose the root cause of the gastritis by direct examination of the organ through a fibrescope. One should never offer champagne to someone who cannot take it, although thankfully that is extremely rare.

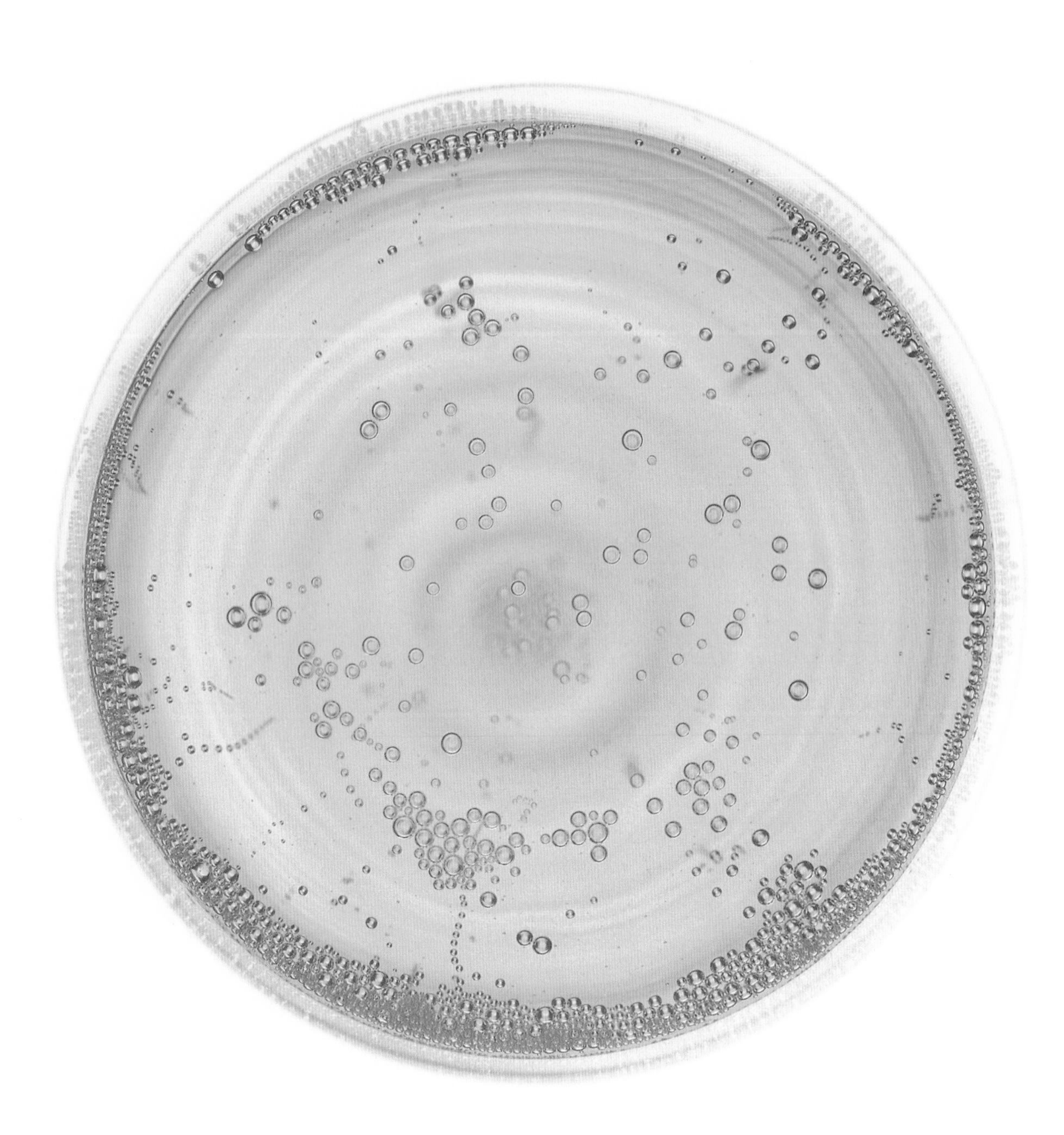

'Noble man never dislikes good wine.'
Rabelais

CHAPTER 15

Lazy Bowel

Jean-Jacques Rousseau never hesitated to prolong his sessions on the throne by several hours, whiling away the time reading and meditating. Neither did Voltaire, who patiently awaited the welcome relief. 'He who, each day, has a satisfactory bowel movement is always a good-natured character,' insisted the author of 'Candide', who advised his fellow citizens to follow his precious recipes to combat constipation in order to live to an advanced age. 'Sometimes I am unfaithful to cassia in favour of rhubarb,' he wrote, but he was also well aware of the virtues of champagne in this area.

Louis XIV's august constipation was such that his pages had to hold a candle until the accomplishment of the royal defecation. Happily, the unruly stools of His Majesty did not prevent him, far from it, from attending to affairs of state from the height of his pierced throne. And this is not a caricature. When the Palatine Princess, his sister-in-law, irritated by the monarch's unending hours of faecal immobilsation informed the Princess Regent of Hanover of this incredible inconvenience at the French court, the latter consoled her and praised the pleasure 'to shit anywhere when the urge catches you'. It was a given that when the Sun King was constipated, the whole court was similarly afflicted. What discomforts would have been avoided if His Majesty's doctors had known that champagne could have alleviated the royal discomfort which kept him glued to the thunder box.

Dom Pérignon

Eureka!

The greatest minds of the Enlightenment did not think it beneath them to perfect and enliven 'the art of making a deposit'. Poets, scientists and even theologians spent a lot of time anal-ysing, in the smallest detail, the million and one stratagems for facilitating the daily offering, all in full public view, of course. This came as a bit of a surprise to the reserved American ambassador, the greatly learned Franklin, who sincerely believed that 'the distinctive character of the French is not to piss alone'. What he meant of course was to defecate. A pity the American scientist had not read 'The History of Shit' by Dominique Laporte, or the deep reflections of Saint-Simon and Molière, on this fundamental problem which show how constipation plagued our ancestors. Clearly, constipation, an equal opportunity affliction, spares no one: famous or humble, yesterday or today.

Fortunately, there is a plethora of remedies for this tenacious condition. Traditional medicine has been aware of the laxative properties of white wine, and particularly of the power of champagne to provide relief to women who complain of discomfort at the onset of their periods. Of course some cases are more serious, even alarming. It would be ridiculous to pretend that a dramatic case of constipation could be relieved by wine, even champagne!

Good sense recommends a prompt visit to a doctor. Only a direct examination with a flexible endoscope would allow a full understanding of the situation and eventually determine the nature of the obstacle.

Constipation is an anomaly in the frequency and character of the stools. If it happens irregularly we should not call it constipation. In fact the regularity and duration of the trouble is more important than its intensity. The physiological frequency of bowel movements varies from one subject to the other. Some have a movement four to five times a week, others once or even twice a day while feeling perfectly well. Whatever their frequency, the stools should remain well-formed, hydrated and soft. Their quantity depends on the vegetable fibre content of the food. A diet rich in vegetables and fruits generates four to five well-formed specimens of excrement and constipation is exceptional.

In true constipation the stools are hard, dry, small in size and quantity, and very difficult to expel, even if the subject has some limited success at each of several daily attempts. Conversely, defecating only once every four or five days is certainly constipation, even if there are abundant stools or false diarrhea. This is cause for concern especially if it is regular and of long duration.

Some believe they have intestinal transit problems when they are simply subject to a normal forty-eight hour cycle. The proper role of the colon is to prevent matter from progressing too rapidly to ensure the recovery of water and mineral salts. While the transit through the small intestine is measured in hours, the transit of the colon takes three or four days.

In small doses champagne has an interesting laxative action and is often effective. However, more than two flutes reverse the action and amplify retention. The pancreas reacts immediately and liberates glucagons, a hormone which slows the movement of the digestive tract. Moreover, excess alcohol always lowers muscle strength and evacuation becomes, perforce, inefficient. This fact is well-known and can be reproduced at will in mice. Excess alcohol always paralyses the digestive enzymes which lose their ability to direct the action of the muscle fibres.

In a person who takes a glass of champagne after the evening meal, one

'Then was the time to think of if when you lay,
Most hog-like, gorging at table, in love with your own capacity.
And so, well may you sit here now:
The latter end of all your delight in this,
That you pummel your belly for the sins your throat committed.'
Agathias Scholastikes (translated by Dudley Pitts)

observes that colonic motility increases slightly, compared to the normal, and digestion intensifies. In a state of intense emotion the discharge of adrenal hormones hastens the transit in one subject in four. A small amount of champagne works for nearly everyone.

Numerous experiments prove that the transit time of the total remnants of a meal is between four and five days in a normal subject, but four to six weeks in a constipated one. It would seem that most people who complain of intestinal sluggishness present in reality a perfectly normal transit, physiologically.

How many of our fellow citizens are constipated? Many, if one judges by the tons of laxatives sold every year. These products even figured on the list of strategic goods forbidden for export to the Warsaw Pact countries. Constipation and its geo-political and military implications!

Statistically, one man in four and one in every two women complain periodically of these troubles. If only they knew that, with a flute of champagne, they could avoid these long hours lost in solitude; they would surely prefer it to their suppositories, paraffin oil, laxative jams and other paraphernalia of pills.

The best remedy is a diet rich in vegetables and exercise. But it is most important to know that every case of constipation in a subject over the age of fifty, especially if repeated, requires an appropriate colonic examination to determine the cause of the blockage. Stool analysis gives a good insight into the process of digestion and on the presence or absence of blood. In general, intestinal re-education is relatively easy and represents an efficient mode of prevention.

From the 18th century onwards, traditional medicine has had recourse to the *champenois* wine of Ay to treat certain forms of constipation. One can find old recipes which advise slices of strawberries, prunes or peaches soaked in champagne to be taken twice a day after meals. The wine should be consumed at room temperature and, as we often repeat, in therapeutic quantities; any excess paralyses the intestine.

'*One day,*' writes Samuel Beckett, '*on returning from the toilet, I found the door of my room locked and my belongings piled up in front of the door. Just to show you how constipated I was at that time...But was I really constipated? I don't think so. Stay calm, stay calm! And yet I must have been; how else to explain these lengthy, atrocious sessions in the loo? I never read, neither there nor elsewhere, I neither dreamt nor reflected and just vaguely gazed at the almanac hanging from a nail...*' But then, thanks to a friend who advised him to take a champagne cure, Beckett never knew again these agonising periods which had devoured up to a quarter of his days.

'I am a beer teetotaller,
not a champagne teetotaller.'
Bernard Shaw

CHAPTER 16

Distension, Flatulence and Indigestion

'Gluttony punishes gluttons. Indigestion was created by God to moralise stomachs.' Had Victor Hugo realised that champagne could help prevent the onset of such afflictions he might not have written this in 'Les Miserables'. When André Gide was sailing up the Logone in a whale-boat suffering from stomach pain, he did not know that the mineral salts contained in champagne eliminate indigestion and that there was no need to 'worry about a slightly malapropos fart'. But he became aware of the curative properties of this effervescent wine and from then on used it like water to wash down his meal of porridge and rice. Romance can wane from indigestion as the belly endures agony. Not everybody is as lucky as the character described by Jules Romains in 'Men of Goodwill': 'At the end of his meal, the Marquess of Lescous belches and farts like a trooper.'

Popular traditional medicine has always recommended champagne for distension. It is very effective against flatulence. The grape sugars and natural carbonic gas it contains accelerate digestion. Over and above its gastronomic charm, champagne has for a long time been a staple medicine.

The so-called 'stomach drop' is in reality a gaseous dilation associated with a temporary loss of motor functions of the muscle fibres of the organ. This phenomenon is often behind flatulence, *'which haunted him well into the night'* (Jules Romains). But thanks to the potassium and magnesium content in champagne, gastric contractions resume and clear the untimely winds as if by enchantment.

What happens when a sip of champagne lands in the gastric cavity? The specific action of the wine triggers an abundant secretion from the stomach glands within minutes. This property has nothing to do with alcohol content but derives from the organic acids. Drinks which have strong alcohol content in fact lower gastric secretion. Experiments have shown that port, with 22 per cent alcohol, and whiskey, with 44 per cent, have no effect on acid production in the stomach. But a good champagne, well-aged and with an alcohol content of 12 per cent stimulates the appetite and encourages the work of the stomach thanks to the interaction of its complex substances.

The higher alcohols diffuse across the gastric wall in six minutes, stimulating glandular secretion and stomach contractions. Various grape sugars also contribute in reinforcing the action against bothersome flatulence, especially when one finds oneself confronted with:

'roast larded with garlic cloves the size of apricots. This mass of meat is surrounded by kidney beans: everybody foresees with apprehension the fireworks their ingestion will provoke, but one has manners; not a whisper is heard!' (Raymond Queneau in Pierrot, My Friend).

Gastric cramps occur as a matter of course in those who smoke too much, drink strong alcohol or those whose mucous membrane has been attacked by a poorly tolerated drug (aspirin, corticoids, non-steroid anti-inflammatories). In these cases it is prudent to abstain from fermented drinks, champagne included, even though some will claim to be able to tolerate it without ill effect. Intestinal parasites are another cause of stomach pain. In these cases, a glass of champagne will neither exacerbate nor calm gastric discomfort. Prudence dictates abstention.

Chateaubriand, for his own part, used it liberally to facilitate a fragile digestion. He also mentions that the Duke of Aumale 'sampled the wine of Ay even before his wet nurse's milk'. Indeed, there exists a charming old custom in Champagne of sprinkling a few drops of champagne on the tongue of the baby.

'The priest has just baptized you Christian with water. I baptize you French, dear child, with some dew drops of champagne on your lips.' (Paul Claudel.)

By extension of course, no ship could be launched without the traditional champagne baptisms to ward off the evil eye. But that's another story!

The food we eat during a meal always presents itself in very complex forms to the digestive tract. Thus the large molecules of sugar from carbohydrates are first broken down into simpler sugar molecules, lipids into fatty acids, and proteins into amino acids. This painstaking digestive work is performed by enzymes, the cells of the internal wall of the digestive tract (the mucous membrane), and the myriads of micro-organisms which compose our intestinal flora.

Paradoxically, if man eats to live, he knows relatively little about the physiology of his own digestion. Nature has fortunately provided us with an animal which resembles us like a brother on the digestive level: the pig. He eats everything and has only one stomach. Humans and pigs are brothers-in-arms in gluttony. This is why the French say 'in every man's heart there is a pig asleep'. It is by studying digestion in this animal with the help of isotope-marked food, and the use of remote controlled capsules to take samples of the digestive content and mucous that our knowledge of the whole process is moved forward.

We observe that the presence of a small quantity of champagne prompts, within a few seconds, an abundant secretion of saliva; the enzymes released help digest wine sugars while activating organic acids. Normally a strong alcoholic drink cuts salivation and dries the mouth. With champagne it is the opposite: the presence of trace elements stimulates the sensory organs in the oral cavity to initiate a vigorous response by the salivary glands. This phenomenon also occurs in the stomach.

In the case of a normal meal, food stays in the gastric pouch for several hours where it undergoes a slow digestive process, so it is not surprising that the slightest impediment results in distension. That can be overcome, in the case of a copious meal including spicy and fatty dishes, by choosing champagne as an *aperitif.*

Our stomach filters its contents towards the intestine in small doses in order to avoid overload. But with three meals a day our stomach is practically never empty and at rest. This has a positive aspect in that drainage from the stomach can be too

Cholic

rapid or too massive and this would put serious pressure on the intestine. Those who complain of flatulence believe their meal stagnates in the stomach whereas in fact it has left the stomach too quickly. In light of these experiments, both in pig and in man, it appears that the gastric transit of food is much slower than was believed in classical theory and is more in the order of twenty-four hours instead of six.

It is likely that the mineral elements and organic acids in champagne harmonise the rhythmic contractions to ensure the desired emptying is accomplished smoothly.

Besides the meticulous work of our digestive glands (pancreas, liver, the miniscule glands of the stomach and intestine) one must emphasise again the importance of the intestinal flora which is absolutely crucial to digestion. Keep in mind that this flora contains over one hundred thousand billion micro-organisms whose only function is to help us assimilate our food. They are ten times more numerous than our body cells! These benign bacteria are like an ocean of plankton bathing the folds of the intestinal wall.

In the past it was believed that these friendly microbes were the source of our digestive problems, while in fact they produce enzymes and vitamins day and night. They play a decisive role in preparing food for absorption by the intestine. Their imbalance or destruction can even be life-threatening. As we have seen before, some of the precursors of these micro-organisms are present in wine. Their presence encourages growth for the necessary renewal of flora. Moreover, the presence of mineral salts like calcium, magnesium and potassium facilitates the contraction of the thin muscle which surrounds the intestinal wall. The organic acids in these mineral salts also encourage bilious secretion.

At this point one must insist on the particular importance of magnesium and potassium in the proper functioning of the digestive tract. Nearly all the digestive processes involved require the energy that these elements provide. As a thermal regulator, magnesium modulates the excitability of nerves and muscle fibres. It is essential in protecting the organism from cold and other environmental challenges. It behaves like a conductor imposing his rhythm on the operation of the digestive tract. All glandular secretions need it. It initiates their flow and ensures their co-ordination. The presence of magnesium explains the beneficial action of champagne in the case of indigestion. However, excessive consumption can lead to vomiting. Moderation, as in all things and, as we shall never tire repeating, is the golden rule.

Our modern lifestyle often induces a magnesium deficit. Industrial fertilizers composed of nitrates and phosphates cause a fundamental imbalance in both animal and vegetable products of high yield agriculture. Moreover, we tend to favour a diet high in meat and we neglect fruit and vegetables which are our main source of magnesium. Cooking methods also play a role in magnesium deficiency. For instance, cooking water, which retains up to 75 per cent of the mineral elements in food, is not re-used in soups or stocks as it used to be. Another surprising reason for deficiency is excessive urinary elimination of this mineral. This happens especially in young women using contraceptive pills and in older people treated with corticoid, diuretic or neuroleptic drugs.

When the muscle cells lack magnesium, the permeability of their membranes is affected. They no longer act as efficient control mechanisms for what comes in and what goes out. Water and salt (sodium) then permeate the inside of the cells in inappropriate quantities and generate swelling which is at the root of intestinal sluggishness. The loss of contractile efficiency explains the distension (or atony) of the intestinal folds which creates in turn an unpleasant bloated and heavy sensation, sometimes interrupted by painful spasms caused by the disorderly contraction of the muscle fibres of the intestinal wall. The digestive glands also fail to follow their regular routines.

And as if this was not enough, the intestinal flora, unable to renew itself and follow its normal cycle, begins to proliferate. This produces another batch of intestinal gas which aggravates flatulence even more.

One glass of champagne contains at least 1mg of magnesium acting synergistically with many other mineral salts. This insignificant dosage suffices, in most cases, to revive the atonic muscle and nerve cells of the intestinal wall. Champagne is rich in grape sugars (glucose, fructose, sorbitol) which also help. They encourage the rhythmic contraction of the intestinal folds and help the transit of food.

The action of magnesium is closely tied in with the activity of other mineral elements, and in particular potassium and calcium. In man, an abnormal drop in magnesium always leads to a drop in potassium and vice versa. As these two salts are of equal importance in the concentration of intestinal cells it is obvious that you should not have one without the other. As luck would have it, champagne contains both these minerals. Anyone drinking a flute to relieve distension simultaneously absorbs these two salutary substances. This fact helps explain why popular good sense always had confidence in the health-giving power of this wine in such situations.

It would of course be excessive to say that champagne constitutes an abundant or ideal source of magnesium. In its original form, as the juice of the grape, it contains only 10mg per litre, or 8mg less than orange juice. But in champagne, as we know, the element acts in concert with all the other beneficial components of the wine to facilitate the complex work of the digestive tract rapidly and effectively.

Since potassium is the main ally of magnesium, it is worth getting better acquainted. Every day, food normally provides 2 to 5mg of potassium from which our body extracts what it requires. This take up is both swift and efficient. The smallest trace of this mineral is immediately located and channelled to top up the reserve stored in our cells. The organism keeps a vigilant watch over our expenditures of potassium in order to be able to confront whatever situation may arise. There are many circumstances which can lead to a substantial drop in potassium levels. As well as being expended in digestive problems of various origins, potassium is frequently eliminated by diuretic drugs prescribed to treat cardio-vascular conditions. That is why it is prescribed in conjunction with these medicines to compensate for its loss. Diabetes and certain kidney diseases are complicated by loss of potassium. That explains why patients suffering from these diseases complain of poor digestion. In the beginning when the deficiency is not very important, there is hardly any detectable symptom apart from distension and intestinal sluggishness. At this stage recovery is rapid if potassium deficiency is diagnosed.

A slight deficiency is quite frequent, notably amongst elderly women suffering from oedema in the lower limbs. Swelling of the ankles may be caused by poor circulation. Here again a milligram of potassium in a flute of champagne produces an effective diuretic effect, while encouraging the return of venous blood towards the heart by increasing the tone of the vein wall. The mineral substances are not only diuretic, they relieve tiredness and, with the help of the wine esters, trigger the release of digestive hormones. Cholecystokinine is one of them, inducing nervous contractions in the gall bladder. In small doses, cholecystokinine stimulates the appetite and triggers ample and rhythmic movements in the intestine. But in higher doses it distends the stomach and cuts the appetite. Thus the positive or negative action of this hormone varies according to its quantity. This mechanism explains why champagne is beneficial in appetite loss and also why it is contra-indicated to drink several glasses at once. At the absurd and suicidal limit, '*pomponette*' – the custom of emptying twelve flutes on the twelve strokes of midnight – is a sure shortcut to delirium tremens!

Champagne is truly a magic potion when one considers that it is able to exploit this physiological process in the manner of this hormone while at the same time supplying the energy and mineral elements necessary for the work. Champagne can digest everything, except itself in excess.

Distension is not, as we think, a simple matter of gas or weakness. The whole organism is implicated. It is surprising to observe that due to its wealth of mineral salts and organic molecules, a single glass of champagne is often sufficient to restore order to the unimaginably complex work of digestion. Bismarck, the Iron Chancellor, is probably one of the best-known victims of flatulence recorded in recent history. Or was it just a display of his martial inclinations? This problem could be very embarrassing for such a prominent statesman. It is said that he treated himself with champagne. He apparently became acquainted with the therapeutic benefits of champagne in 1871 at Versailles when he was named Chancellor of the Empire. That year he vanquished France but succumbed to champagne. Thereafter, to control his windy outbursts, the Chancellor continued to drink a glass of champagne after each meal until he reached the venerable age of eighty-one. History does not say if he passed away before fulfilling his goal: '*A man must not dream of dying before he has drunk five thousand bottles of champagne and smoked a hundred thousand cigars.*' Political correctness does not apply to larger than life characters. Or was it a case of '*you can have too much champagne to drink but you can never have enough!*'

Let us not forget that champagne drunk for health has nothing to do with quantity. Quite the contrary. As long as it is of the highest quality, a little does indeed go a long way.

'Some champagne,
To harmonise
With the flow of life.'
Tu Fu

CHAPTER 17

'Crise de Foie'

'His face lost its vivid brown complexion, announcing an onset of hepatitis, the disease of vigorous temperaments or of an aching soul, whose affections are upset.'

Balzac believed that the local priest reacted with a liver crisis to every frustration! 'All the misery in the world has its seat in the liver' is the accepted belief, at least in France. This deeply-rooted opinion maintains that hepatic inadequacy and liver crisis are the source of all health problems.

In fact, there is no biological evidence to justify accusing this organ of a wide variety of gastric discomforts (nausea, bloating, congestion). Most of the troubles people complain of under *'crise de foie'* have in fact nothing whatsoever to do with the functioning of the liver.

Although our compatriots firmly believe that the liver is the source of all sorts of maladies, we should remember that subjects suffering from imminent cirrhosis, whether of viral or toxic origin, rarely present the sort of symptoms commonly believed to signal liver disease.

The myth of the *'crise de foie'* remains firmly entrenched in the land of Gargantua. The French think it prudent not to worry *(se faire de la bile)* so as avoid a *crise*. 'One could easily accommodate heartbreak, if the mind or the liver did not falter.' Such statements demonstrate the bad reputation of this extraordinary gland, the most complex in our body. Despite the progress made in understanding its physiology, the so-called *crise* continues to wreak havoc in every level of society. One French man in every two is affected. Two thirds of French women, if not more, complain of it all their lives. Given the dimensions of this 'epidemic' in the popular imagination, it is no surprise that there are close to one hundred and fifty remedies aimed at curing this tenacious affliction. Some even think the malady is hereditary and some families have been stricken for generations!

Alas, despite their number, neither remedy, nor any specific therapy, has ever proved effective. At least they all have one undeniable quality: they are not toxic. Amongst the many sufferings attributed to this poor organ some are probably relieved by medicines said to 'fluidify the bile' or 'tone up the hepatic function'. But in most cases it is the placebo method that brings the cessation of these symptoms.

In truth, the liver is a wonderfully vigorous and incredibly resistant organ. It is not only the most solid but also the largest in our body. It weighs 1.5kg. It ensures all the multiple vital functions of our body, currently estimated at about about five hundred. Unlike other organs, the liver is unique in having two circulatory systems. An arterial network stemming from the hepatic artery brings oxygenated blood and removes waste. A venous network called the portal system supplies the organ with raw materials collected in the intestine and stomach. The liver must extract the nutrient substances, transform and store them. To these two circulation systems we must add a third formed by the bile ducts.

A complex network of dedicated channels drains off the bile secreted by the liver. This greenish liquid is composed of cholesterol and bile salts which play an essential role in the digestion and absorption of fatty foods. The liver keeps a portion of the half litre of bile it produces everyday in a small pouch (the gall bladder) which sits just beneath the liver's lower edge. This reserve is only used during digestion. Bile plays the role of a detergent dissolving fat to make it easier to absorb.

Owing to its high content of magnesium ions and carbonated salts, champagne activates the biliary flow allowing for the efficient elimination of a great number of harmful substances. It has long been observed that the wholesome substances of champagne contribute to the regularisation of this function by activating the biliary circulation and the intestinal transit, and encouraging a deficiency in liver function.

The liver has other important functions. For example, in the case of a fracture the liver can increase protein synthesis and hasten healing of the bone. The liver also plays an important role in immune defence. It is endowed with an army of giant cells, which behave like ogres. These are the Kupffer cells, responsible for destroying microbes and toxic molecules, as well as ageing red blood cells. Day and night these voracious and cannibal monsters surround, swallow and digest the invaders. Any serious liver disease weakens this precious defence mechanism. The liver then fails to neutralise the nearly fifty different toxins produced by our own body. They accumulate in the blood and unfailingly disturb brain function.

Our liver is a wonderful organ ensuring most vital functions; biosynthesis of essential substances, energy production, elimination of toxic waste, immune defence are its daily tasks. One understands why the gods in their fury condemned Prometheus to have his liver devoured by eagles.

Research has not yet explained the role of the liver in its own disorders. For a long time it was thought that poor functioning of the liver ducts was behind a whole array of varied and elusive ills. Opinions are divided, some claiming that the liver discharges too much bile, others that it is rather biliary retention that causes indigestion and pain. We speak of stasis, atony, irritability, hyper-evacuation, dyskinesia... and these more or less enigmatic terms lead us to believe that the mystery of the liver has been clarified. The formerly fashionable practice of duodenal intubation and surgical intervention on the valve controlling the opening of the main hepatic duct did not result in a solution either.

As a popular remedy for *crises de foie*, the beneficial action of champagne derives from its slight acidity and from the quick action of its components on the duodenum. At first, champagne acts directly on the mucous membrane of the duodenum by provoking instantaneous release of digestive hormones. Secondly, it excites the nerves which encourage the work of the liver and the pancreas. It seems that the cause of a *crise de foie* lies in the poor division of labour between nerves and hormones. Their failure to synchronise and cooperate synergistically, not the disease, is the most likely cause of the digestive problems which can be eased in most

Crise de foie

cases by the mineral salts and organic components of champagne.

It goes without saying that a diseased liver, whether from viral, toxic or alcoholic causes, will be unable to perform its titanic tasks. It is thus fundamentally important not to offer champagne to cirrhotic patients even if alcohol is not the root cause of their predicament.

'Wine, so divine, that the most beautiful names are pushed to describe you.'
Abu Nuwas

CHAPTER 18

Aerophagia

In polite society one speaks of eructation, burps, aerophagia: 'The spasmodic swallowing of air, a fairly common neurotic habit that may lead to belching and stomach pains', while in more popular circles one simply calls it belching. The oral regurgitation of gases is a perfectly natural physiological act, affording relief to a distended stomach. It is not belching which is abnormal, but the inability to belch. In this case a certain heaviness and bloating could inconvenience the victim even to the point of suffocation. Apart from babies whose anxious mothers prod burps from them after suckling, etiquette frowns on public displays of belching even though it is highly beneficial for the belly, and good behaviour even demands we avoid the very word lest it evoke the indecent act. It is not enough to avoid the disgusting act, one must also mask it, gloss it over, or sweeten it with sumptuous euphemisms when it becomes absolutely necessary to evoke it. Yet to belch is also a highly cultural act. In certain countries it is required politeness from an honoured guest. Flaubert complained about the rude and unsophisticated ambassador who 'would not dine with the Turks, because the Turks belched up your nose.'

When one finds oneself, like Raymond Roussel, under the hot and humid climes of equatorial Africa, it is the only way of ensuring a sound digestion, especially after eating a well-spiced roast: *'From time to time, the women let go through their mouths, widely ajar, some formidable burps which, soon, multiplied with a prodigious speed. Instead of dampening these repugnant noises, they seemed to flourish with a crescendo, in a rivalry of sounds and fury.'* (African Impression)

After a meal, the volume of ingested food expands and distends the wall of the stomach. In atonic and flabby stomachs expansion can take on extraordinary proportions. This is sometimes referred to as gastric prolapse, a strange Newtonian notion which would lead you to believe the stomach can fall like an apple from a tree! In reality, it is a simple distension of the gastric pocket when the muscular wall has lost the ability to contract. It is often this type of lazy stomach which is prone to eructations. But there are also gastric spasms which occasionally provoke a little belching or a hiccup crisis. Usually the ability to expel gases provides instant relief and progressively reduces hiccups.

Excessive food intake or swallowing too quickly triggers a more important gastric evacuation through the pylorus. Then, as the food arrives in large quantity and somewhat abruptly in the duodenum (the first part of the small intestine), a reflex occurs to immediately block the evacuation upstream by closing the pyloric valve. Everything happens as if the intestine did not want to be overloaded and raised a barrier to the emptying of the stomach. The closure of the pyloric exit generates undesirable gaseous emissions.

The composition of the food also influences the speed and importance of evacuation. Undigested food, whether too fat, too raw, or poorly chewed, is often massively repulsed during the hour following its ingestion and a prolonged blockage of the pylorus can ensue. That is when the sensation of heaviness and the compulsion to belch appears. That was the case of the poor fellow who swallowed too fast and too copiously: *'Alarmed, one already feared a truffle indigestion, when mother nature came to the rescue. Mr. Simonard opened his large mouth, and violently belches out a single fragment of truffle, which graciously landed on the tapestry...'* (Physiologie du Goût).

Brillat-Savarin was right: thanks to this providential belch, our gourmet-gourmand had been able to cut short many hours of discomfort.

The crux of the problem lies in the correct functioning of the exit valve responsible for evacuation. Curiously, when the stomach is empty the pylorus remains open or slightly ajar so that gastric air can move without hindrance and wind is rarely a problem. But as soon as the first gastric mouthful hits the duodenum, the pylorus closes. The peristaltic waves may well prod it on, but they encounter an even more tightly closed lid. The role of the pyloric ring, which is composed of both circular and longitudinal fibres, is to stand guard and regulate the quantity of food allowed into the intestine. The pylorus does not function as an autonomous organ, but as one element of the stomach-pylorus-duodenum complex, which regulates the rhythm of digestion to avoid digestive overload. Quite frequently, the exit door remains open though the stomach might well be full. Despite this, the food only crosses over in small intermittent spurts. The process occurs as if the stomach, knowing the work rate and capacity of the downstream end, relies on the evacuation mechanism to fine tune the outflow in keeping with a harmonic rhythm.

In a person who absorbs several aperitifs, a strange to-ing and fro-ing happens between the upstream and downstream functions. The stomach, full of liquid, often alcoholic, expels its content toward the duodenum which allows only a minimal quantity in and pushes the excess back towards the gastric cavity. Beer imbibers should be thoroughly familiar with the belching phenomenon after downing two or three glasses.

What happens when one drinks a glass of champagne to aid and abet digestive performance? The higher alcohols quickly diffuse through the gastric wall and enter the bloodstream, without the need to pass through the exit door. Nearly 40 per cent of the volatile substances of the wine are absorbed in this fashion in the first ten minutes, provided the individual limits himself to one glass only. One further glass and the reverse happens. A certain amount of the mineral substances and some of the grape sugars are exploited immediately to reinforce the activity of a tired stomach. At the beginning, the amplitude of the contractions removes excess air through the mouth and relieves distension. The muscle fibres regain strength and coordination. The root cause of gastric wind is really the uncoordinated functioning between upstream and downstream.

The pleasant and beneficial sensation experienced by the subject who consumes champagne in moderation does not in fact accelerate the evacuation

'Good wine is a good familiar creature, if it be well used...'
'Othello' Shakespeare

process, as previously believed, but mainly harmonises the opening of the pylorus when stimulated by the peristaltic waves originating from the upper part of the stomach. Apparently the beneficial effect of champagne on aerophagia is more perceptible when it is absorbed during or after a meal. It also depends on the composition of the meal itself. However, an excessive dose of alcohol unfailingly paralyses the delicate functioning of this system and blocks the exit valve. It is thus incorrect to say one can drink liberally to combat aerophagia.

Research has demonstrated that the presence of gas in the drink has no influence on the rhythm of evacuation. This disproves the erroneous belief that the carbonic gas of champagne aggravates eructation. Quite the contrary: the gas is an active ingredient in the stimulation of the gastric contraction.

The speed of evacuation depends on the biorhythm of the digestive tract and varies sensibly from morning to evening. In most cases the stomach evacuates twice as slowly in the evening as in the morning. This phenomenon is due to hormonal secretion cycles, which follow a 24-hour pattern. It also explains why belching is more common at night during digestion. Ideally, that would be the most propitious moment to administer a flute of champagne, which would soothe any discomfort in minutes.

Recent research has discovered that sometimes a second command centre exists in the lower part of the stomach. Its parasitical waves interfere with those coming from the upper part and disorganise the rhythm of evacuation. The stomach gets confused and often balloons up to the point of impeding breathing.

Proust suffered much from poor digestion caused by gastric overload and endured painful session of aerophagia. He was advised to take a glass of champagne to overcome these crises.

To belch is neither a bad habit nor excess air stuck in the gastric pouch. It is the result of a dysfunction in the emptying of the stomach which as we have described, rests on a complex mechanism. One might well ask why we need a plethora of nerves, hormones and organs to regulate the outward movement of food. It is because our stomach acts as a kind of bandleader imposing a regular and balanced flow to the intestine as well as controlling caloric intake. Many people complain of still feeling full several hours after a meal. This stems from a discordance associated with prolonged gastric evacuation. The discomfort results from food overload and an excess of fatty substances. From this viewpoint, belching represents an alarm call dispatched by an engorged duodenum on reception of the first mouthfuls. But the stomach is on watch and knows perfectly well what is in store.

It is reassuring to know that however unpleasant this discomfort might be, it can quickly be remedied by the salutary components of champagne, at the right time, in therapeutic doses. But beware! One flute too many creates further harm.

The ethyl alcohol present in the drink plays absolutely no role here. It is thus quite wrong to think that a strong alcoholic aperitif can help digestion.

Modern research in physiology has now established that champagne, in small amounts, is most beneficial in the highly complex functioning of the digestive system. The constant interaction of the many forces at work is never gratuitous. The subtlety of champagne is virtually unique in bringing harmony to all physiological functions.

'Good wine makes good blood,
Good blood causes good humour,
Good humour causes good thoughts,
Good thoughts bring forth good works,
Good works carrieth a man to heaven.
Ergo, good wine carrieth a man to heaven.'
John Minshen

CHAPTER 19

Final thoughts

Well then, what is the message contained in a bottle of champagne, *'la dive bouteille'*, the divine bottle, so dear to Master François Rabelais, *'Docteur ès Médecine*?'

'En vin est vérité cachée': in wine the truth is hidden. He liked to play with words and with the etymology of the word wine, also derived, according to him, from the Latin *'vis'*: 'force'.

As we have reviewed in the previous chapters, the therapeutic force acts on the physiological level in a process which science allows us to progressively understand better and better. But that is only one dimension and certainly the one which was our focus all along these pages. But champagne is also much more, to be explored another time, by acting directly on the senses and the soul, as anyone with a normal palate and nose has been able to experience for himself. By infusing *'joie-de-vivre'* and lifting the spirit, it aids and abets the cure of the body; a truly holistic and symbolically-rich beverage indeed. Beyond the chemical complexity of its constituents what explains the potency of its effect and the power of its message? In champagne one can savour *'the message transmitted, year after year, by over one hundred generations of wine makers. It is the condensate of thousands of roots probing the innermost secrets of a soil. It is the sublimation of a summer's warmth. It is the fruit of a year's toil by the vine grower. It is the laughter of the grape picker, the energy of the grape crusher, the tender attention, vigilance and competence of the cellar master to craft the masterpiece. All that is good in man is transfused into his wine: courage, joy, faith, perseverance, love, and optimism. All that is beautiful in nature is expressed in wine: warmth, strength, light, colour, and mystery...Wine is matter transmuted into spirit, which you can observe shimmering and sparkling through the crystal of the glass.'* (Louis Orizet)

'It also embodies a tradition, the continuity of life over and beyond the cycle of seasons. It binds the generations by overcoming time.' (Alain Montandon)

This remedial nectar for body and soul promotes harmony and thereby wholeness of the personality, the very foundation of a vigorous immune system and of a resilient state of good health. Which synthetic chemical molecule or pill can make similar claims?

Let us not forsake the magic potion, which has served us so well and for so long.

'Do your best, and keep in a state of joy,' said the great Spinoza, probably the simplest and best piece of preventive medical advice ever given. A daily flute is all you need.

' *Trinck!*' whispered the divine bottle.

Cheers, to your very good health and may the force be with you!

'Remember, gentlemen, we are not just fighting for France, we are fighting for champagne'.

Bibliography

Albert B. et Coll. : *Molecular biology of the cell,* Garland, New York, 86.
Bernier J.J. et Coll. : *Les Aliments dans le tube digestif,* Doin, Paris, 88.
Benoit O. : *Physiologie du sommeil,* Masson, Paris, 84.
Binkley S. : *Une enzyme épyphysaire qui mémorise le temps,* Scientific American., March 85
Bonal Francois : *Le Livre d'or du champagne,* Ed. Grand Pont, Lausanne, 84.
Bruneton J. : *Elément de phytochimie et de pharmacologie,* Lavoisier, Paris, 87.
Buckley R.H. et Coll. : *Food allergy,* Journal of American Medical Association (JAMA), vol.8, nb 72, August 83.
Carles J. : *La chimie du vin, 'Que sais-je?',* nb 968, Paris, 84.
Casarett and Doull's : *Toxicology (3rd edition),* Ed. Macmillan, New York, 86.
Cautin et Coll. : *Le Coeur est une glande endocrine,* Scientific American, April 86.
Corless J.K. et Coll. : *La Physiopatholgie hépatique,* JAMA, March 84
Galet Pierre : *Cépages et Vignobles de France,* vol. I, II, III, Galet, Montpellier, 62.
Dufy-Barre L. : *Les Hormones de l'hypothalamus,* La Recherche, nb 160, nov. 84.
Durang G. et Coll. : *Les Enzymes,* Gauthier-Villars, Paris, 82.
Duteurtre Bruno : *La Science du champagne,* La Recherche, nb. 183, Dec. 86.
Etievant P. et Coll. : *Le Goût du Vin,* La Recherche, nb. 193, Nov. 87.
Korn H. : *La libération des neurotransmetteurs dans le systême nerveux central,* Medecine/Science
John Libbey, Oct. 88.
Lehninger A. : *Biochemistry (3rd edition),* Worth Publisher, New York, 86.
Le Tacon Francois : *Les Mycorrhizes : une coopération entre plantes et champignons,* La Recherche, nb 166, May 85.
Maury E. : *La Médecine par le vin,* Edition Artulen, Paris, 88.
Nordmann R. et Coll. : *Alcool et radicaux libres : données actuelles,* Medecine/Science, John-Libbey, Paris London, Jul. 88.
Nyanken L. et Coll. : *Flavour research and alcoholic beverage,* Alko Symposium, 1984, Helsinki.
Rapoport J. : *La Biologie des obsessions,* Pour la Science, nb 139, May 89.
Rives Max : *Les Origines de la vigne,* La Recherche, nb. 53, Feb 75.
Sasson A. : *Les Biotechnologies : défis et prouesses,* UNESCO, 1983.
Wurtman R. : *Les Aliments qui modifient le fonctionnement du cerveau,* Scientific American, June 82.
Youvan D. et Coll. : *La Photosynthèse,* Scientific American, Aug. 87.

Documentary annexes

The Miracle of Grape Variety

Like human beings, every vine cultivar has a name, history and ancestors. That elicits respect when it comes to prestigious lineages, capable of producing champagne. Soil, sun, the art of the wine maker, and the three basic varieties (Chardonnay, Pinot Noir and Pinot Meunier) contribute to an equal extent to the personality, colour, aromas and texture of champagne. Independent of the very important ageing phase in the cellar, one must keep in mind that it is above all the quality of the vine plant which conditions finesse, 'bouquet', flavour and the longevity of the wine. The vine jungle is absolutely fascinating when one penetrates it. Like cereals, these plants had colonized all far corners of our planet, including the least fertile, and under the most inhospitable climates.

It takes at least three years before a vine plant starts producing and ten years for it to reach full capacity, which lasts on average, from forty to fifty years. Its cultivation requires exacting care, as two stocks of the same variety, separated by a path, can yield two different grapes, and thus two quite different wines. From pruning in winter, to the choice of harvesting time in autumn, each action of the vine grower will affect the quality and quantity of wine produced. To get to know the vine cultivar is to enter its soul.

Chardonnay

Let us start with the first lord, Chardonnay, probably the most courted plant in the world. It embodies those precious qualities so much sought after by growers, wine makers and gourmets.

Its name differs according to the places where it is exploited. Chardenai, arnaison, morillon, roussot, little Saint-Mary... are some of the most common appellations, but in Champagne, it is 'pinot blanc chardonnay' and 'epinette' which are the most popular. Although the plant was born in Burgundy, it can thrive in a variety of ecological conditions and has become the most famous cultivar in wine-producing countries across the globe. Modest and undemanding, it requires only a chalky and relatively poor soil; a fertile ground or too much humidity would be counter-productive. All growers cultivate it, either for champagne or other reputed wines.

Thanks to its natural vigour, chardonnay is generous and tolerant if treated with respect. In a region where the growing season is short and where the winters are intensely cold, which is the case for Champagne which has a semi-continental climate, the major concerns for growers are spring frosts. They must also drain the ground, in order to prevent rot, which might occur after the autumn rains. Fortunately, the grateful chardonnay knows how to pay back its dues with a relatively early ripening.

To fight off the cold, the growing technique, derived from experience and tradition, consists of increasing stock density: nearly eight thousand plants per hectare. Furthermore the importance of pruning, called 'long stalk pruning' allows the rich sap to concentrate in the grapes by avoiding too thick a foliage. A well-cultivated vineyard yields sugar rich grapes which, after fermentation, provide good quality wine. The best yields can reach up to fifty hectolitres per hectare.

Chardonnay easily accepts various grafts, as long as they are robust, but it is vulnerable when rainfall is too plentiful. White rot and grey decay, induced by the proliferation of viruses and mildew, threaten. When harvested too late, the juice acidity can sometimes drop suddenly, which may lead to a 'lack of spine'. This can also happen if the season is too hot. Apart from these dangers, the noble vine plant usually delivers an array of various high quality wines, well-bred for wine-making and ageing. It is one of the rare wines, endowed with an astonishing malleability, which lends itself with good grace to receiving the full imprint of soil, season, winemaker and time.

The aromas of chardonnay remain discrete and full of nuances, somewhere between apple and melon. Occasionally, an abnormally high alcoholic content adds a slightly 'nutty' tonality, but this is rare if the champagne is of good quality. Whoever has come under the spell of good champagne will keep its lingering memories for life. Chardonnay requires patience before surrendering the secret of its subtlety.

Ampelography is the science devoted to the study of vine plants. In his extensive three-volume treatise, 'The Vine Plants and Vineyards of France', the great ampelographic botanist, Pierre Galet, leads us to believe that chardonnay is a particularly old plant of our patrimony. It would seem that it originally descended from white Muscat. That is why some of its aromas evoke, at times, the fragrance of its ancestor. And yet this lord of the vine was born in the modest cradle of the village of Chardonnay, in Maconnais. It only colonised Champagne from the 19th century onwards. As with most prestigious titles of nobility, the lineage is subject to debate. Lebanon and Syria, for instance, which have been cultivating similar plants (meroueh, obaideh) for a long time, claim that they are the ancestral stock, only introduced in Europe later by Crusaders and monks.

The Champenois and Chablis vineyards represent three quarters of the fifteen thousand hectares devoted to chardonnay in France. The merit of the talented Champenois vine growers, not forgetting those of Bordeaux, has been to raise the technique of 'assemblage', the blending of various grape varieties to the level of an art form, to produce a refined and inimitable palette. Without chardonnay, pinot meunier and pinot noir would deliver a rather thick and unctuous taste; they lack the delicate sprightliness of the former. That is the reason why true champagne marries the fruitiness of pinot meunier to the richness of pinot noir, balanced by the grace of chardonnay. The ideal French ménage-a-trois! In Champagne, the vineyard of every classified village contributes its own tonality and colour to the overall symphonic orchestration. There is little in common between the frivolous charm of the grapes of Avize and the seductiveness of those of Cramant, between the acidulous 'Côte des Blancs' and the vivacity of Mesnil-sur-Oger. These are the characteristic contrasts, which meld and harmonise the aristocratic texture of blue-blooded champagne.

The growers are unrelenting in their quest for perfection. Yet morality is not universally shared and some do blend their must with inferior plonk and hasten to mask their 'champagne' in bubbles and alcohol to piggyback on the reputation of this exceptional product. There are champagnes and 'champagnes'. Caveat emptor! This is where the vigilance of the control organisations is indispensable to police the trade.

Pinot meunier

Although widely cultivated in Champagne, with more than ten thousand hectares, pinot meunier only assumes the role of a brilliant second. It knows how to remain discreet, until it contributes its own tonality. In fact, it is the grape which truly embodies the vitality and youth of champagne. Its deeply indented leaves often reveal a serene appearance. The quality of this juice is patience, biding time to suddenly express vigour. One tends to look upon it as a shy cultivar, a second fiddle to chardonnay, a poor country cousin and yet it is absolutely indispensable. All the same, it leads an independent life, until called upon to contribute its juvenile fruitiness which reinforces or brightens, depending on circumstances, the composition of champagne. One must be careful however not to overdose at the risk of 'greening' the wine.

On the biological level, this plant shows extreme resilience to frost. That is why it is widely used in Germany, where it is known as 'black riesling'. Its Champagne location is a natural, given the chalky soil and climatic conditions.

Why is it called 'miller pinot'? Simply because the fuzzy leaves seem to have been powdered with flour. The bunch of grapes is very compact, making it vulnerable during rainy periods. Water retained between the grapes encourages the development of parasitical mushrooms: vine-mildew (oidium).

The distinguishing botanical feature of this plant is a late flowering. That does not prevent maturity before harvest as it builds very quickly during the summer months. Rain, even prolific, does not affect the pollens of this plant, which delivers a steady fructification and yield. This is not the case for pinot noir, often prey to flower abortion.

Actually, pinot meunier is the object of intensive study all over the world but especially in California, where the world famous Oenological Institute nurtures the dream of producing someday a great champagne on the shores of the Pacific.

Pinot noir

Tradition says that pinot noir is a cultivar which knows its master. Indeed it only reveals itself to wise and persevering growers, who invest the necessary time to probe and discover its idiosyncrasies. To cultivate, and turn into wine, nothing can be left to chance. This is not a forgiving plant for novices and amateurs.

The susceptibility of the plant is legendary, especially in soil which has been poorly prepared, drained or is lacking in chalkiness. Under such conditions it is ravaged by all kinds of diseases: mildew, oidium, grape rot, grey rot. Pinot noir requires vigorous grafting and the ability to resist parasites and mildew. It also requires substantial pruning to avoid coiling, one of the favourite viral fixation points.

Unlike chardonnay, which travels and adapts everywhere, pinot noir is a homebody. Transplantation into a new milieu implies such an investment in work and patience that very few attempt the venture. Its localisation in certain European countries (Germany, Italy, Switzerland...) is the result of centuries of effort by generations of persevering and obstinate growers.

The metamorphosis of the aromas of pinot noir is very strange. Sometimes the young, soft wine produces a fragrance of strawberry or raspberry, and at other times it remains dull and odourless. After ageing, it explodes as if by magic. An array of aromas,

Labour of Love

incredibly complex, marries the fragrance of violet to the hint of truffles. This fairy-like abundance comes from the dynamic fluidity of its genetic patrimony. It is the hallmark of the pinot family, be it white, grey or black. Admittedly, the genealogy of these cultivars remains puzzling for most genetic ampelographers. The plant life of these mysterious vines is in fact rather short - twenty-two years compared to the average forty. And yet, the family comprises numerous varieties, over one thousand two hundred have been surveyed, created by cutting and grafting or cloning. It seems they all descend from a common ancestor known in the Middle Ages as 'pinot vermeil'. Historians discovered that this title of nobility (mentioned in the register of a hospice in Burgundy dating from the 14th century) proves that the wine from this vine was already in use as a remedy. Of course, pinot noir goes back even further. The Gallic peasants had probably obtained the rootstock from a cross between imported and local varieties. It came as something of a surprise to the Romans when they invaded the region. Ever since, pinot noir, a lord in the kingdom of vines, has remained unchanged. Its progeny however is bountiful: pinau, salvagnin, pignol, rouci, noirien, klevner, cortaillod, blauburgunder... not counting bastards, usurpers and pretenders who also claim part of the lineage.

This extreme proliferation of varieties stems from the intrinsic qualities of the cultivar, as well as the need to find local mutants, more resistant and better adapted to local conditions. That results in an extended and prolific family of wines.

All pinots noirs do not necessarily give thick-skinned grapes, rich in tannins and anthocyanes. A range of different champagnes illustrates this diversity of origins. Bollinger, for instance, comes from a non-grafted pinot noir of very old stock, which even survived the phylloxera crisis! Its bouquet strangely evokes that of a smooth burgundy. It provides a hint of the champagne that was drunk in the old days. The oenological evolution has been phenomenal over the past hundred years and the degree of selection and refinement has never been higher.

In general, pinot prefers a cool and dry climate. The later the harvest, the richer the juice and the more complex the road to maturity. When the season is too wet, the grower often chooses to harvest early in order to avoid the risk of mildew. On the other hand, it is very sensitive to spring frosts. All these difficulties make pinot far too challenging for inexperienced vine growers.

Is it not curious that the art of champagnisation consists in making a white wine with the red juice of pinot noir? It is this prowess which provides each vintage with its personality and longevity. If one knew how difficult it is to prevent the must from being coloured by the red pigments of the skin, it would be easier to understand how each wine maker possesses, in this matter, a secret raised to the level of an art form. This quasi-magic and ritual exercise, transmitted through generations, is jealously guarded by each champenois cellar and deeply anchored in the hearts of those engaged in the constant dialogue with the vine.

From the stock to the glass, so many obstacles and unsparing efforts! To fight off frost, there are many devices, including a fuel heater, covered by a chimney or an apparatus expelling warm air or water. The flowering, in May, is always at risk were the temperature to drop suddenly. The terrible frost of 1985, not only destroyed the harvest, but also 25 per cent of the plants. Such extensive damage requires several years of remedial investments to restore the vineyards.

These three so-called 'noble' cultivars belong, as we saw initially, to the vitis vinifera specie. Their notoriety, to which little can be added, rests mainly on the organoleptic quality of their grapes, which are better suited than any others. This choice has not been made at random, but is the result inherited from centuries of technical and cultural experience.

The downside is their sensitivity to climatic risk and diseases. These have been kept at bay through an array of countermeasures. The most spectacular, in effect a first in terms of 'organic biological weapon', was the use of phylloxera-resistant grafts. This elegant solution avoided the recourse to insecticides! But there is no single, ideal, ecological shield against the numerous viral assaults. There are at least thirty viral species which threaten the vine plant. To fight off these cryptogamic diseases of leaves and fruits, one needs chemical products. The efficiency of sulphur to fight oidium and of copper to fend off mildew is now well-established. Despite this progress, however, their usage, even on a minimal basis, is not without negative side effects. The asymptotic ideal is, naturally, to cultivate in an ecologically sound manner to the best extent possible.

The creation of biologically viral-resistant plant varieties has been attempted for a long time. Several generations of botanists, geneticists and selectors have searched intensively but, despite all efforts, no one has, up to now, been able to find the vine plant not requiring fungicides.

Let us not forget that, in nature, a vine also reproduces via seeds. The pips have an overriding mission in the perpetuation of the species while, in cultivation, sexual reproduction is bypassed as a source of unexpected mutations amongst the cultivars under exploitation. In general, the sowing of pips harvested from a specific plant yields an abundant progeny, more or less similar to the original parent. But, in a subtle fashion, they differ one from the other by a whole set of characteristics, so that none is totally identical to the initial parent.

This is quite different from grafting (in effect, cloning), which reproduces identical individuals; sexual reproduction from pips, on the contrary, creates different individuals. It is possible to take advantage of the diversity engendered by this mode of multiplication by sorting out, from the plants issued from sowing, those presenting advantageous properties. Some cross-breeds can result from this selection, which are superior to the mother plant in respect of at least one specific point. However, this selection process is extremely tedious and time-consuming and discourages many geneticists.

As an example, after more than fifteen years of experimental trials in both greenhouses and on the ground, the researchers of the National Agronomic Research Institute (INRA) have only managed to obtain twenty-three new vine plants, sixteen of which are able to produce table wine. This meant a long and very costly undertaking. The creation of a superior vine plant owes more to miracle than hard work. It is in the daily dialogue and interface that the human genius scrutinises the smallest details of the plant in order to penetrate its secrets and then nudges it towards the most desirable goal.

This creative selection by cross-breeding, which has always been practiced by vine growers, has resulted in cultivars, which are endowed with sufficient positives to offset the negatives. The imbalance, common to all plants, is then counterbalanced, at least qualitatively, by the joint cultivation of other cultivars and the blending of the grapes into a harmonious whole. That is very much the case for champagne wine.

To the extent that grape resistance and quality are not two incompatible notions, it would seem that a certain compromise is acceptable. This middle of the road approach leads to a rational equilibrium between the development of rootstock resistant to viruses and mildew, and one requiring only minimal treatment; it is a reasonably efficient approach. A first attempt has already been made in several countries. The principle rests on copying the ancestral technique of grafting, but *'in vitro'*, in the laboratory.

It has been discovered that the branches, formed on a plant attacked by viruses can become resistant if the branches are grown at a temperature of thirty-seven degrees for a few months. Life in a heated atmosphere (thermotherapy) has conferred immunity to these virus-prone plants. To gain time, reproduction is carried out by cutting and growing the branches in tubes, in a soil enriched with growth factors (auxins, cytokinins...). This process eases the *'in vitro'* micro-cutting reproduction. It is not the only research approach in the fight against viruses. Microbiologists have also managed to create variants of a rootstock by cellular cloning of the buds. They can, thereafter, select from the resulting plants those, which present advantageous characteristics such as resistance to viral toxicity or to chemicals in various guises. We can safely predict the arrival of new and interesting varieties of vine plants requiring minimal fungicides.

For the time being, however, only prevention is effective. Experienced vine growers make sure that the vineyards do not suffer from a deficit of magnesia or potassium, which causes browning of the leaves. They also try to avoid excess calcium, a source of chlorosis. Other precautions consist in minimising the use of toxic herbicides. Spoon-shaped leaves and twisted young shoots generally result from the application of phyto-hormonal herbicides, which stimulates these anarchic phenomena.

This is the daily struggle of those wine growers bent under the vine branches - an incredible investment of time and effort for which the return is measured in blood - the grape juice! If you listen carefully, you will hear the melody of the leaves, rustling amongst the vines in the breeze:

' I know what toil, and pain and sweat you thole,
Under the roasting sun on slopes of fire,
To give me life and to beget my soul—
So I will not be thankless to my sire...'
Les Fleurs du Mal (Baudelaire)

Vine and Mushrooms: a Marriage of Reason

Since when did one see the noble vine condescend to marry a mere common mushroom? Strange partnership; and yet, this union against nature has lasted ever since the vine appeared. Though not an idyllic couple, it has remained rock solid through the ages. It is obviously an arranged marriage, forced by the incredible pressure from the trials and tribulations of extra-aquatic life.

Two living beings, belonging to different species, can unite in a common body for their mutual benefit. It is what biologists call 'symbiosis'. All superior beings do, in fact, lead a symbiotic life by harbouring in their organism other supportive species. Even humans have not escaped from the universal law of interdependence! Literally, hundreds of billions of micro-organisms live in our guts – in silence, for most of the time! Indeed, our precious intestinal flora helps us digest while benefiting from our hospitality.

The vine plant, like most superior green plants, has to co-exist symbiotically with invisible mushrooms. These weave a dense net of filaments, intimately enlacing the roots of their partner. Their nuptials take place deep underground, hidden from the prying eye. Botanists modestly call this secret embrace 'mycorhiza', which simply means 'root-mushroom' (from the Greek *'myces'* and *'rhiza'*: mushroom and root).

Why would the vine, a higher plant, accept this forced arrangement? It is because it needs the hard-working mushrooms to help absorb the mineral substances present in the ground, especially the indispensable phosphorus. The mushrooms take up the nutritive elements and pass them on to the host-plant. They are, in effect, the suppliers of the mineral salts contained in the grape juice and it is to them we owe the beneficial virtues of wine.

At the beginning of life, when the first plants lived strictly in an aquatic milieu, they could absorb the mineral substances dissolved in water directly. Their life was as independent as that of current seaweeds, and they could take whatever was needed from the nourishing environment. But the situation changed totally when plants colonised the land, where mineral salts exist primarily in an insoluble state. Those first plants faced a dilemma: either die, or accept a compulsory cohabitation with mushrooms, which are uniquely able to weave a web of filaments around their roots in order to extend their absorption surface. So, for several hundred million years, most green plants have been taking advantage of this strange union.

Curiously, if the host plant cannot do without the mushrooms, they, on the other hand, can be entirely independent. Some even act and behave as confirmed bachelors! They are from the family of oyster and morel mushrooms, which know best how to exploit decaying plant. But when mushrooms form a couple with a specific plant, they conversely benefit in turn from the sugars, which are synthesised by the plant chlorophylls.

There are, at least, a hundred different species of these helpful mycorhizal mushrooms which teem in the soil. They are present on every continent, in union with nearly all plants, and particularly fruit-bearing trees. The roots of every vine plant are covered with an uncountable number. But these parasitical lovers are so minuscule that they are unseen, except under the microscope. That is why their role has been misunderstood for such a long time. Few biologists took an interest, as they were scarcely known to them. Then, about a century ago, their presence was discovered by the German biologist Frank, although, initially, he had no idea about their role. That was left to Noel Bernard, in 1900 in France, who, at the time, was studying orchids.

The life of the vine totally depends on this mycorhizal synergy. However, modern viticulture, with its increasing use of fertilizers, contributes to an elevation and concentration of soluble mineral substances in the soil. In so doing, the vine grower has, unknowingly, introduced a new evolutionary factor. Confronted with this overwhelming cornucopia of mineral wealth, the vine plants are in a position to do without their cumbersome partners. The vine plant is thus regaining some freedom, which is not without a deleterious impact on yields and the quality of grapes.

In the soil, the filaments (or mycelium) jealously coil around the roots of the plant to flourish in knots and sacks gorged with nourishing sap. It is truly the intimate penetration of two living beings, through the close contact of their surface and cells. That is how the ardent mushrooms feed the languorous vine; they literally wrest from the depths of the earth the least soluble and less mobile mineral salts to enrich the sap. The quality of the juice is intimately tied to their active presence. Without their painstaking work, the biological composition of the grapes would be a liquid, void of any dietetic value.

Phosphorus is a basic substance for all living beings, be they plant or animal. This mineral salt constitutes the basis for the cell membrane. It also represents the backbone of the genetic material in the nucleus of every cell: desoxy-ribonucleic and ribonucleic acid. Phosphorus also intervenes in the production and regulation of energy in the cellular factory. Poorly soluble, its concentration remains extremely weak in the soil. The absorption rate of the vine plant is further lessened in chalky ground, which is porous and water-deficient. It is easy to understand, then, the providential role played by these omnipresent mushrooms which can deliver to the plant most of the phosphorus available in the ground. In short, the denser the mycelial network around the roots, the more the plant will be able to absorb phosphorus and all the other mineral elements such as zinc, copper, magnesium. The presence of trace elements in the juice is the direct result of this intense subterranean affair between mushrooms and vine plant. Their relatively insignificant mass is endowed with a colossal energy, which can leach from the earth the mineral salts indispensable to the host-plant.

This wonderful synergy, or rather cohabitation, was clearly demonstrated by the researchers of INRA. By tagging the soil with radioactive phosphorus (P32), they noticed how the fuzz of the mushroom helps the plant to extract the phosphorus located up to twenty centimetres away from its roots. Even better, in soil which does not contain enough soluble phosphorus, the mushroom immediately releases special enzymes (acid

The grapes of sickness

'My poor grapes if you don't get better it won't be because of me...
I've really done my best to treat you!'

phosphatase); this secretion helps to extract phosphorus from the rock to make it soluble. That explains why the concentration of this element is three times higher in the mushroom than in the vine. Even curiouser, these hard-working mushrooms are also farsighted. They permanently build up an important reserve of these important mineral substances in their cells. In case of deficiency or drought, it is they who feed the vine with their stores.

How does the transfer of the nutritive substances between these two partners happen? To harmonise the outgoings of the vine plant, it would appear that there are two forms of inventories: one immediately available, like a current account, to satisfy the immediate need of the growing plant; the other, a savings account, loaded with complex phosphorus but hard to mobilise, and which only yields parsimoniously.

The job of the mushroom is not finished at that. It must also supply nitrogen and other mineral substances. The nitrogen fertilizer, in its mineral form, is first collected by the mushroom fuzz, then transformed and converted into an amino acid (glutamic acid) by the enzymes of the mushroom. The latter then introduces the amino acid to the cells of the vine roots. In return, the mushroom receives 20 per cent of the sugars (glucose, fructose, saccharose) produced by the leaves of the host plant.

In a vineyard, the microscopic mushrooms of the various plants weave a full-fledged underground network. This common system enables the transfer of nutritive substances from one area to another. A vine planted in an unfavourable spot is able to receive material help pumped from another area. Here, the mushroom displays a relational role, ensuring social coherence amongst the plant population. Each vineyard behaves, in a way, as a living entity, held together by this underground informational network, which supports its unity and personality.

How could the vine resist a partner so devoted and indispensable? In recognition of services rendered, it provides in return, not only vitamins but also aphrodisiac substances, which stimulate the growth of the mushroom's reproductive organs! This obviously has nothing to do with a marriage of convenience. The state of arousal is such that the mushroom responds by discharging a growth substance to stimulate the growth of roots, leaves and tendrils. Through this mutual and passionate declaration of love, the more the vine embellishes, the more the mushroom protects it with poisons, which annihilate other bacteria and nefarious moulds present in the soil. The symbiotic mushroom behaves like a natural fungicide, which augments the resistance of the plant against diseases. This is why well-maintained vineyards are less vulnerable to parasitical assaults.

Numerous factors can disturb the harmony of this solid couple. Too much fertilizer, too broad based disinfectants and poor ground drainage are a considerable hindrance to the development of the mushroom fuzz. But it is mostly human intervention which disrupts the balance of the couple. By enriching the soil with too much nitrogen and phosphate fertilisers, one increases the vine yield but at the expense of sugar availability for the root system. The mushroom, deprived of this energising food, weakens and does not discharge its customary duty, leaving the door open for predators to launch their attacks.

In light of our knowledge of the intimate life of the vine plant, would it be feasible to make it accept other possible suitors or protectors in order to increase its resistance and overall well-being? After so much time spent together, the partners are used to each other's company. In nature, any mushroom is not just compatible with any vine plant. In France, as well as other countries such as the United States and Japan, researchers are hard at work classifying the various symbiotic mushroom strains. They are then selected and attempts are made to enhance their performance through genetic manipulations. For the time being, it has not been possible to grow these mushrooms independent of the host plant. They wither and disappear in an artificial environment. The trend is towards producing small quantities in special fermenting solutions. The mushrooms are then fixated in alginate granules to seed the plantations and vineyards with a view to avoiding the use of fungicides. The trials are ongoing and the goal of biological culture getting closer.

In general, the introduction of new strains introduces an element of competition with existing ones. The first results obtained by this new variety of living fertilizers/fungicides have proven most encouraging. It is likely that artificial mycorhization will become part of the general panoply of vine-growing techniques in the not too distant future. The ultimate goal is to produce champagne without any anti-viral products, which are still required for the treatment of vineyards at present. This is now within reach. This new methodology is a natural and elegant way to do without fungicides and chemical fertilizers. It seems obvious that a true biological cultivation of vine plants requires a thorough understanding of the biology of these mycorhizal mushrooms, which are an integral part of the soil-plant system. Were one to neglect the role of these discreet components, it would lead to regrettable cultural mishaps and, by the same token, negate the beneficial effects of the wine. This is of prime importance for vineyards located on chalky soils, which is the case for champagne. Their relatively poor phosphorus and sulphur content is a real handicap for the grape's well-being. Under such conditions, research hopes to revitalise the soil through the inoculation of symbiotic mushrooms adapted to the prevailing characteristics. The important thing is that these imported strains maintain themselves in the humus and multiply normally.

Another technique, applied in California, consists in first producing plants in green-houses by inoculating the pre-selected mushrooms right from the start. They are then transplanted to a vineyard cleansed of its underground micro-flora. This process is vital for the large nurseries, which produce young plants in test tubes in an artificial and aseptic milieu. Subjecting them in the cradle to this forced union matches them with an efficient protector for the future.

The other approach is to diversify the genetic structure of the various vine plants, to enhance their defence mechanisms against parasites. Up to now, the fight against viruses is essentially chemical (phytosanitary products), cultural (pruning and soil drainage), biological (micro-organisms against pests) and genetic (selection of resistant plants). None of the current techniques is sufficient, on its own, to solve all the problems. Their complementary usage and the adoption of appropriate strategies might someday overcome the viral assaults on the vine.

We are only beginning to understand the importance of the symbiotic relationship between the vine plant and its underground companion. More and more, botanists and ampelographers are moving in the direction of first protecting the micro-flora which cohabits with the plant by using adapted methods (soil aeration, minimal use of chemical fertilisers). This is a preventive stance against potential aggressors. It might also prove possible to stimulate the vigour of plants by inoculating them with improved strains of symbiotic mushrooms. A true biological cultivation, without fungicides, is currently being developed in the secrecy of laboratories, which consists of identifying the best possible party to consort with the vine. A well-wed vine becomes resilient and defends itself energetically against viral predators. About fifteen defence proteins (or PRP for Pathogenis-Related Protein) are then produced in the affected leaves to intoxicate and discourage the aggressor.

We are far from knowing all we need to comprehend the daily struggle of the plants. They have been able to innovate and develop very ingenious mechanisms to ensure their survival. It is these natural defence processes that researchers are trying to understand, preserve, enhance and stimulate.

The Magic of Yeast

As soon as the grapes are ripe, bacteria and moulds are jumping in to seize the opportunity and have their feast. Some are producing the 'noble rot', much sought after in the production of the famous wines of Sauternes. But, in Champagne, the vine growers carefully eliminate all mouldy grapes to avoid contaminating the must.

The presence of yeasts and bacteria on grape skin is a normal phenomenon. With the arrival of autumn, each grape carries on its skin at least ten billion spores of these micro-organisms. A light wind blowing over a vineyard during the harvest carries with it about twelve million spores per cubic meter of air. This extraordinary dispersion also comes with a remarkable vitality. Well-protected, the spores of wild yeast strains always remain alive and can germinate even after twenty-five years.

In their hundreds of billions then, yeasts and their consorts make a living on ripe fruits. The simple pressing of the grapes is enough to put them in direct contact with the juice sugars. That is the ideal medium for the yeasts to grow, multiply and, in so doing, bring about natural fermentation.

Under a strong microscope, these alchemists look like small round cells with a nucleus. A yeast cell measures barely five microns in diameter. It is enveloped by a rigid double-walled membrane. What differentiates yeast from bacteria is that the nucleus of the latter is not isolated by a nuclear membrane. On the other hand, the nucleus of yeast is surrounded by a spheric partition, which resembles a pouch containing chromosomes and which carries its genetic patrimony. The cellular nucleus of yeast possesses thirty-four chromosomes, against forty-six for man – a minimal difference between us and these uni-cellular beings. Sexually, the love life of yeasts is strangely similar to that of our own sexual cells.

When the ambient milieu is rich in nutritive substances yeast thrives and multiplies quickly by burgeoning and giving offspring, which all carry thirty-four chromosomes, spread in twin lots of seventeen chromosomes. However, if the external conditions become more difficult, the parent yeast produces offspring with only seventeen chromosomes, half of the maternal inheritance. As with humans, there are children of either sex which nature keeps in check as they are united four by four, two males and two females, in a small pouch, to facilitate future unions. These are the real sexual cells of yeast - also called spores - always ready to serve, scout like, and fuse again as soon as the environment lends itself to it.

The marriage of yeast children, to reconstitute the full genetic inheritance (17 + 17 = 34 chromosomes or 17 pairs of chromosomes) is of vital importance to biotechnology. This knowledge permits the selection and cross-breeding of various strains in order to obtain new ones, endowed with specific properties to improve some of the particular wine characteristics.

Yeasts belong to the vast family of microscopic mushrooms. Again, it is they who, after having helped the vine to produce fruits, transform sugars into wine. Uni-cellular mushrooms are all around us and hyperactive. They were the first to colonise our planet and were its reigning masters for several billions of years. We owe them our very existence. Most of the yeast strains that man has domesticated belong to the genus 'Saccharomyces', sugar mushroom in Greek.

Since prehistory, humankind has used the fermentation process to conserve and improve the quality of its food: bread, wine, cheese, yoghurt, but also sausage, ham, brine, sauerkraut, tea and vinegar.

The unrelenting and beneficial activity of the minuscule yeasts was even compared to the vitality of faith in the 'Parable of leavening':

'The kingdom of heaven is like unto leaven, which a woman took, and hid in three measures of meal, till the whole was leavened' (Matthew 13-33). *Although for Hebrews, all food had to remain pure and azym, Saint Peter still recommended to the Corinthians this renewal rite: 'Purge out the old leaven, that ye may be a new lump, even as ye are unleavened.'* (Epistle to the Corinthians 5-6).

Later on, the Galatians of central Asia Minor were similarly encouraged to fortify their vacillating faith: *'A little leaven and the whole dough ferments.'* (Epistle to the Galatians 2).

Paradoxically, yeast, mentioned forty two times in the Book of Books, represents two contradictory forces. It is feared as a source of impurity and respected as a symbol of vitality in the new Alliance. All of these historical documents are proof enough that humankind has always used the invisible yeasts, whether on an alimentary or spiritual level; and this well before their existence was ever discovered. It was only a little over a century ago that Pasteur, at the request of the Lille brewery, solved the mystery of the process of fermentation and initiated the era of microbiology. Since then, the various beneficial strains of yeast have been quickly catalogued and studied.

It is certain that the need to pour insecticides into vineyards has ruptured the frail balance of the flora of indigenous yeasts. For that very reason, it is imperative to constitute a complete collection of the micro-organisms which live spontaneously in the various regions of Champagne. Biologists may then select them at a later date for the best possible use.

The techniques of genetic engineering aim to improve certain varieties of industrial yeasts, which have already been stabilised. Thanks to the knowledge developed about wild strains, the hope is to graft new properties onto domesticated yeasts required by vine growers and oenologists. For a wild strain to be selected, it must be effective in the production of aromas (heavy esters). It should, furthermore, be able to pursue the fermentation process up to extreme temperatures, resist excess alcohol while consuming as little as possible of the nutritive elements of the wine, and create a slight mellow condition through the presence of glycerol and ethanol. On the other hand, it should not produce sulphuric, acidic or mercaptanic compounds. The development of a yeast strain is a long undertaking; up to now, the rare strains domesticated by man are the result of centuries of experience and incredible hard work.

If the selection rules are so rigorous, it is because juice and wine are environments hostile to the development of bacteria. Only certain strains can function in these biological liquids, while others are ruthlessly eliminated and yield toxic by-products. Thus, an inappropriate fermentation, instead of developing aroma, can generate intolerable smells. For the yeasts to function in optimal conditions, the must should present an acceptable level of acidity. Its normal pH is around 3,5 while the yeasts prefer a slightly less acidic milieu at 4,5. Further, the phenol derivatives of must, insecticide residuals and the inhibiting substances coming from the fermentation itself, can all stop the enzymatic reactions.

Researchers are attempting to fine-tune varieties which are adapted to oenological imperatives; but the micro-organisms are much smarter than previously thought. During multiplication, even the selected strains often mutate and modify their tactics. The twists and turns of yeast are unpredictable and can sometimes transform must into a stinking mess. Even the tamest bacteria can suddenly rebel. That is why biologists try to understand the causes of their rebellion to help prevent it.

In nature, as well as in the milieu of culture represented by the grape juice, the environment is never stable. Yeasts must thus adapt to all changes in order to ensure their survival. They know how to do this, by co-ordinating the activity of enzymes. They can even produce new enzymes in order to exploit unknown substances; or also adjust or slow down the secretion of those which are no longer adequate. This adaptation mechanism is commanded by their genes, which regulate the required strategy in accordance with the laws of natural selection.

When the must is of good quality, which is the case during sunny years, yeasts are presented with an ideal quantity of sugar (such as glucose) with six atoms of carbon. Their enzymes break up one after the other the link between the carbon atoms. The molecular structure of glucose, thus ruptured, releases energy and yields carbon, which is used by yeast to construct its own body. The remainder of the carbon is eliminated in the form of carbonic gas (CO2). It happens that the must becomes too sugar-impoverished and that, as a consequence, the available carbon decreases. In such a crisis, the yeasts reduce their consumption and block the workings of their machinery with phosphate molecules. Yeast has normally over three thousand enzymes at its command in its cell. Over one hundred of these are temporarily immobilised by the lack of raw materials but will pick up again when the conditions improve. This phenomenon explains certain unforeseen reactions, when the fermentation process is partially suspended. What is at stake, then, is to gain control over the action of certain enzymes. Work in this area proceeds by selection: change in the milieu

'What... you're treading bare foot!'
'So what!... You wouldn't want us to do it in our dancing shoes!'

of the culture followed by analysis of the yeast response to the new conditions. In its own modest way, biology hopes to help the wine maker avoid nasty surprises and tame the capriciousness of these micro-organisms.

Besides the few well-stabilised industrial yeast strains, there are also wild strains- a highly prized spontaneous micro-flora to which we owe the aroma of certain great vintages. This discreet flora is also involved, during the maturation process, in the reactions of microbial association and antagonism, which occur sequentially in the wine.

Up to now, bacteriological research is mostly focused on the few dominant strains and on those responsible for moulds and rot. Many species have been unjustly considered as simple 'contaminants' without any influence on the quality of wine. Pasteur, who already foresaw the importance of the relationship between the various yeast strains, has brought to light the importance of the close interdependence existing between the various colonies of micro-organisms.

Contrary to popular belief, champagne also ages at the production stage. Biotechnology can follow the maturation process, thanks to the electronic microscope. We know that the second fermentation occurs in the bottle and that this process leads to the *'prise de mousse'* (foam formation). Over time, the deposit of yeasts, created towards the end of the foam formation, will patiently 'make' the wine in the midst of this nutritive environment. The enzymes favour an ageing process of a biochemical nature; silently, the yeasts disappear, one after the other. Their autolysis frees organoleptic substances, which contribute to the perfection of the wine aroma. A well-aged champagne is a liquid full of energy, rich in molecules with superb revitalising properties.

Under the electronic microscope, yeasts can be observed, gorged with substances extracted from the wine and stored in vesicles. Their membrane is swollen and dimpled, and the cellular nucleus is the seat of an intense biological activity. This granulation indicates that the yeast cell is operating full out and synthesises new specific molecules in a recipe which is the hallmark of every distinct family. These observations show that the ageing on rack enriches the wine with two kinds of volatile components. The first derives from the vine plant and stays unchanged. The second is produced by the micro-organisms during fermentation and ageing. As an example, for the wine to exhale a faint aroma of green nut, it must release a complex component formed by dimethyl-tetrahydrofurane dione. This shows the titanic task performed by these minuscule organisms.

The progress of microbiology is progressively helping wine makers understand the mystery of this spontaneous environmental flora and channel its evolution in the right direction. That makes the study of microbial ecology of prime importance. It opens the way to further diversification and enrichment off the palette of pleasing vintages.

Some organoleptic considerations

'I have been drinking champagne for over thirty years, and have never found fault with it.'
'Memoirs of a Parisian bourgeois' (Dr. Veron 1856)

What substances does champagne contain to warrant such devoted loyalty? That is the question in France, and abroad, for devotees of the nose; those endowed with an organ, subtle enough, to track the volatile components of the wine in its last retrenchments. These molecules are the chemical carriers of the elusive aromas. But their study represents a difficult task, requiring the utilisation of most precise equipment. And although negligible in quantity, their role is absolutely essential to the quality of the wine.

As these molecules are unstable and disappear quickly, analysis is delicate, despite the numerous possibilities offered by biotechnology. As usual, knowledge is the prelude to constructive action.

How many volatile constituents are there in a glass of champagne? Up to now, six hundred different varieties of molecules have been identified by gaseous chromatography. This research has been pioneered notably by the Oenological Institute of California, which systematically studies all the renowned brands of champagne. The result was published in a major survey called: 'Research on the flavours of wine'. Other research centres, such as the Helsinki ALKO (also famous in its own right), are also interested in the composition of wine. Their periodic publications concerning the biochemistry of fermentation are works of references in oenological sciences.

It would be going overboard and fastidious to list the hundreds of molecules which make up aroma. For the sake of simplicity, one classifies them according to their chemical nature into eleven big families. Amongst them are: the esters, aldehydes, higher alcohols,

'These grapes look sick, be very careful Adélaide, they might be contagious!'

terpenic alcohols, acetates, ketones, phenols, hydrocarbons; and finally those unclassifiable groups, labelled 'others' which include: sulphured bodies, amines, amides, nitrogen elements, mercaptans, heterocyclics. All of these derivatives are susceptible to change according to the variation in temperature, time and conditions of conservation. Many other constituents remain unknown to this day. In general, one knows that the presence of carbonic gas gives a certain spiciness; that alcohol creates a burning sensation; that ions of sodium (Na^{+}) and potassium (K^{+}) are behind a slightly salty taste; and that glycerol and ethanol, as well as glucose and fructose, provide a sweet sensation.

Each component of the wine engenders a perception, olfactory and gustatory, of a fragrance and flavour, which corresponds to it. Their combination defines the personality of the product. Furthermore, some molecules can generate several aromas simultaneously, either on their own or in association with other chemical components. Everything hinges on these ephemeral associations, on their interaction with the organs of taste and smell and, in the last resort, on the cultural interpretation of the taster.

Aromas can raise our emotions and memories from the depths of forgetfulness as Proust reminds us: *'But when from an old past nothing survives, after the death of beings, after the destruction of things, then only, more fragile yet more vivacious, more intangible, more persistent, more faithful, taste and smell still linger for a long time, like souls, remembering, waiting, hoping, over the ruin of everything else, supporting unfailingly, over their impalpable mist, the immense monument of memory.'* (Swann's Way)

If the memory of a smell does not carry with it the context in which it was perceived, how can one explain the memory of an old event? The mechanism by which these volatile substances act upon our senses and memory is most intriguing. To penetrate the mystery, one must obviously understand the synthesis by which these aromatic components operate during the making of champagne; unfortunately, that is not yet the case, despite all attempts.

In the first stage, smell and aroma are born from the biochemical reactions, triggered by the volatile molecules at the level of the olfactory receptors located at the top of the nasal passage. There, about one hundred million specialised cells weave, with their tentacles and receptors, an amazingly tight network of traps covering about two square centimetres. Their mission is to intercept the aromatic molecules in order to send an electro-chemically coded message to the brain.

When inhaling champagne, the volatile substances of the wine penetrate directly through the nostrils, to stimulate this little olfactory zone, where the sensation of fragrance will be brought to life. On the other hand, when it is *'en bouche'*, in the palate, swarms of aromatic molecules climb through the back passage to reach the top of the nasal cavity. Thus perception produces the sensation of aroma. All of this sensory activity has in fact nothing to do with tasting, but results from the excitation of the taste buds by the soluble substances of the wine.

In the subtle universe of the senses, it is smell, which plays the preponderant role in the appreciation of organoleptic quality. Our sense of smell is indeed endowed with a phenomenal faculty of discrimination; it can differentiate in a selective fashion between several thousand fragrances. Over thirty thousand aromatic molecules are easily detected in our ordinary life. That is why, the 'nose' of an oenologist is such a wonderful apparatus that no piece of machinery, however powerful, can ever hope to emulate.

In general, when the taster notices a particularly delicate flavour in the palate, it usually comes from a good balance between esters and higher alcohols. Frequently, a high content of fatty acid esters is the mark of good quality champagne - which is not to say that the addition of esters to mediocre champagne will improve aroma.

It has also been observed that a champagne without a distinctive organoleptic character often contains too much methyl-butanol, a kind of complex alcohol. Paradoxically, a first-class champagne can also contain a similar amount while still offering an exquisite aroma. Analysis has shown that certain champagnes, aged in good conditions, are rich in cinnamic ethyl molecules produced and released by the micro-organisms surviving in the wine. But it is absolutely impossible to recreate this fruity note by introducing this ester in another champagne.

The symphonic spell of fragrances and tastes is confusing to many researchers, despite their superb and expensive machinery and methods (mass and infra-red spectrometers, nuclear magnetic resonance, isotopic micro-analysis), which are capable of detecting aromatic substances to a nanogram (or a billionth of gram per litre). Though the nasal acuity far exceeds the performance of a machine, this sort of analysis is still indispensable when it comes to diag-nose a 'wine sickness' in order to cure it.

Strangely enough, if the gift of a 'nose' is indispensable to distinguish the exquisite from the ordinary, water remains essential to taste in order to savour correctly. All great tasters know that, to enhance the savours of a great vintage, it is advisable to have a sip of water from time to time in order to neutralise the stimulation of the taste buds. A great water does not thwart a great wine; on the contrary, it releases it from the mass of flavours and allows subtleties to vibrate and finesse to come through. You do not move with impunity from a lobster *'aux fines herbes'* to a singing white *'con allegrio'* without refreshing the taste buds anew.

Water acts as a catalyst for aromas! All gourmets know that an occasional sip, at the right moment, re-launches taste and pleasure, like a caress between two embraces. By its own very virtues, water allows the gastronome to rediscover the *'robe'* and bouquet of wine, and thereby better appreciate and redefine the beauty of this beverage. Good wine deserves good water.

In the universe of aromas, the less abundant molecules are not necessarily the least dynamic. A terpenic alcohol, like alphaterpineol, injects a slight perfumed and bitter sensation. Its content in a full-bodied champagne rarely reaches fifteen micrograms per litre. And yet, it makes it robust, underpins it with a gamey structure and confers a distinct originality.

This example highlights that the most aromatic components are not just those which are adequately concentrated in the wine, but also have sufficient vapour tension, so that their molecules are easily released to make an impression on the olfactory receptors; but not all the volatile constituents have the same immediate effect. As the spectrum of olfactory nuances is almost infinite, the nose discriminates, over and beyond the aroma of such and such a substance, its variations and metamorphoses, as soon as it changes its concentration or its union with other aromas. It happens that one fragrance masks a second to release the blooming of a third, which otherwise never would have had a chance to express itself. That is the challenge of wine appreciation. Thus, in the rare champagnes conserved in oak casks before the second fermentation, one often observes a mixed fragrance emanating from isoborneol, with a faint austere note of camphor. On such a personal note, it is no longer the taster who chooses the wine, but the wine which seduces him!

Our knowledge in this field is still very shallow. Despite the large number of volatile components already isolated, we still cannot define the types of wines by analysis. Apart from a few wines, the chemical differences between the various varieties of champagne are almost undetectable. It would be quite presumptuous to say that we understand the mechanism through which the wine constituents affect aroma. Many of the factors which characterize the originality of a brand cannot be determined with our current techniques of analysis, while an oenologist will describe them very precisely thanks to his exquisite sense of smell.

During the phase of ageing and maturation - the conditions vary with the kind of champagne being made - wine progressively loses its fruitiness and gains bouquet. The aromatic substances, which are formed during this lengthy period, represent the post-fermentation aroma. We know that it is the whole cellular machinery of bacteria which drives, molecule by molecule, the alchemy of aromas. Some work has brought to light the degradations and reworking of esters and acids by hydrolysis. Besides, diffusion through the fibres of the cork contributes in no small part to perfect the formation of aldehydes and acetals. Further transformations occur among the aromatic structures. The birth of a single black current fragrance involves no less than nine hundred different chemical components; those of an iris flower nearly seven hundred.

The aromatic substances that we know are only colours of a vast palette, which the artist manipulates and juxtaposes according to a thematic scheme. This work of genius is the work of the 'nose'. In the shadowy light of his cellar, surrounded by numerous samples of *'cépages'* and *'crus'*, but also references and blends from previous years, he blends, doses, composes, sniffs, inhales, savours, tests and interrogates. Suddenly an idea arises and he rotates his glass in the air to get a whiff of the evanescent fragrances. He modifies nuances, varies proportions, creates combinations and takes note of his impressions. A real architect of the fragrance medium, he reinforces here, lightens up there, frames, models, plays the harmonics and assembles contrasts until he has found balance and light.

At the beginning of the last century, the prevailing belief was that the aroma of wine came from an 'oenantic ether'. Towards the middle of the century, about fifty aromatic components had been discovered; that number has now been multiplied by a hundred. Today one counts over thirty thousand kinds of molecules implicated in this sensual voyage. No doubt we shall find out more, especially concerning the interrelationship between aromas. This asymptotic quest of the indefinable still makes sense by allowing the oenologist to further raise the bar of excellence and to ensure the regularity and consistency of the organoleptic quality of champagne.

Initiation rites

Technical appendix

Ethanol and its action on the digestive system

Thanks to the great strides made in biochemistry, we now know that ethyl alcohol (ethanol) is a very subtle molecule. An energizing food, although not if one believes nutritionists, a psychotropic substance used for millenniums to stimulate the mental faculty, this ancient medicine is also a drug of unpredictable toxicity, as it varies from one individual to another.

Ethyl alcohol does not act alone in champagne. Its action is, in reality, modulated by the other alcohols and esters. Amongst those, one counts already twenty-one terpenoid alcohols, twenty higher ones and fifty-two esters, that we know of! That gives an indication about the magnitude of the problem one faces when studying the problem objectively. Clinicians, biochemists, neurologists, psychologists, toxicologists, epidemiologists, botanists, linguists, historians, jurists... are all analyzing the phenomenon and all with their specialised terminology. Over the past few years, a common international reflection has allowed research to pursue a more rational focus and to establish bridges across the various jargons. This new endeavour has also brought down a few walls and broached subjects until now taboo.

On a purely experimental level, research work has long been confronted with a major difficulty: the absence of an animal model. It is almost impossible to reproduce this or that symptom in a laboratory animal and then treat him with champagne! Unlike man, nearly all animals, chimpanzees excepted, refuse instinctively to absorb any liquid containing the slightest trace of ethanol, even when deprived of drinking water. There are, however, a few species of rats and mice, resulting from genetic manipulations, which are a bit more inclined to accept it, but their intake never exceeds their elimination capacity. And none so far has been able to tell us whether they slept better or ate better after a few drops of champagne. At best, they can shed marginal light on the action of alcohol in minute doses. One has also administered ethanol by intravenous or intraperitoneal injection, by force-feeding or by confining animals in an atmosphere containing alcohol vapour. Overall these experiences concern a specific toxic element, ethanol, which has little to do with the very complex nature of wine. This approach is somewhat removed from reality and targets more the spontaneous and excessive consumption by man. Thus we are none the wiser when it comes to the medicinal properties under study.

It has been found that an excess of ethanol inhibits the two nerves responsible for the regulation of evacuation. The many local hormones are overwhelmed by an immoderate intake. The first one out of action is motiline, which normally induces the functioning of this complex in regular transit. The other one, gastrine, is paralysed by an over abundance of aperitif. This hormone, in principle, reinforces the amplitude of contraction of the muscles of the gastric wall. Confronted with this chaos, other hormones, instead of helping, further the disorder. Such is the case for glucagon, secreted by the pancreas, which goes awry, increasing the spasms while simultaneously blocking the pylorus. In this sabotage, it is aided and abetted by an accomplice, somatostatin, which also comes from the pancreas. Another important hormone taking part in these contractions is cholecystokinin. It is also inactivated by the alcohol. Conversely, other chemical agents become excited (endorphins, neurotensine, prostaglandins E and I...) and have a further effect to constrict the pylorus. This physiological mechanism was first studied in detail in the laboratory by the team led by A. Cortot. They revealed the nasty side effects brought on by wine and alcohol in relation to the amount consumed.

Furthermore, an excessive intake of ethanol induces the formation of acetaldehyde. The latter, in conjunction with other substances elaborated by the nerve cells, metamorphoses into a morphinic product, capable of paralysing the regulatory action of the nerves which orchestrate the effort of the stomach during this critical moment.

Champagne contains an infinitesimal amount of special proteins (secretogogues) formed over the years by the yeasts and bacteria during fermentation. These substances can stimulate the gastric secretion of the glands situated in the stomach wall. The gastric secretion induced by a flute of champagne can reach up to 97 per cent of its normal capacity, or sixteen times more than that induced by a normal meal.

Experiments conducted by the research team of Singer, working with various beverages, have shown that an alcoholic degree over 20 per cent progressively neutralises the hormonal molecules secreted by the stomach. Over 30 per cent, alcohol degrades practically all the digestive hormones necessary to the normal functioning of the stomach. Even hydrochloric acid secreted by the stomach loses its efficiency in decomposing protein fibres.

Thus, in helping to bring balance to the gastric hormones, champagne contributes to the harmonious functioning of the whole process. And thereby, regularity is gained in the evacuation process, thanks to the orderly rythm induced in the peristaltic waves, which control the contraction of the gastric wall. Relief of belching comes partially from this mechanism; the harmony brought to all secretions seems to contribute to a normalisation of the zones which generate electric commands; most likely, through an active circulation of the electrolytes (potassium, calcium ions...).

If some feel much relieved after sipping a champagne flute before a meal, it comes down to the action of inositol, which can catalyse the enzymatic reactions, thanks to its energetic synergy with calcium and phosphorus. These elements act like real tonic substances on the nervous and glandular structures of the digestive tract and the energy supplied by these nutrients favours the orderly operation of the stomach. It is most likely that this enzymatic mechanism is the major influence in reducing the symptoms of flatulence, which were traditionally addressed with champagne.

Thanks to its alkaline pH, saliva neutralises the acidity, which prevails in the gastric mucous membrane. Its composition, besides enzymes such as amylase and lipase, is mostly growth factors, blood group proteins and secretory immunoglobins. All of these molecules play a role in orchestrating a harmonious function of the gastric glands.

Once in the gastric cavity, champagne will immediately undergo a complex process in order to be rapidly channelled towards the intestine. Within a few minutes, a substantial portion of the higher alcohols and esters cross the gastric wall, to enter the blood stream while the still intact plant molecules undergo the assault of hydrochloric acid, which breaks them down in order to become digestible. Meanwhile, the stomach has already received the energy required to perform its task. Enzymes, including the powerful pepsin, partake in the break up of complex substances into smaller fragments. The rare, friendly bacteria, which live in the stomach, also benefit from the reinforcement provided by the wine. It contains not only elements which encourage their growth, but also yeasts which enrich the flora activity.

The 'Metallo-enzymes'

We now know that the dialogue between the different defenders of our organism, the lymphocytes for instance, is carried on by a set of molecules, certain of which are enzymes combined with a metal atom. These chemical messengers are called 'metallo-enzymes'. Over the past years, great strides have been made in our understanding of this field thanks to the fruitful collaboration of two fundamental sciences: physiology and nuclear physics. In the light of this work, it has become much easier to follow the pathways of the isotopes of such and such an element in the communication between the agents of our immune system.

Every molecule of Vitamin B12, for instance has within it an atom of cobalt which is the true centre of gravity of this vitamin, and provides it with the necessary energy and specificity to accomplish its mission. From this perspective, cobalt behaves like an indispensable trace element for the functioning of our cells. There is barely 1 mg of this metal in our body and yet that is largely sufficient for its effect to become catastrophic in case of excess. These cobalt elements are particularly concentrated at the level of the pancreas. But they do not always act on their own: their action is often combined with that of other metals (manganese, zinc, copper...) through the interplay of enzymes. Vitamin B12 is not the only carrier of this metal, many enzymes also fix it in order to direct the work of calcium. When associated with manganese, cobalt, which is a catalyst, not only helps our cells to mature, but also participates in the regulation of our immunological reactions. This metal is normally found in most foods. It would seem that the daily requirement for this mineral element is quite minimal (0,1 microgram only). It quickly becomes toxic at high dosage and triggers skin, cardiac and digestive problems through the increase of blood cells. In the past, certain beer brands contained cobalt salts, specifically added as anti-foaming agents, and generated massive intoxication. That illustrates the dangerous toxicity of these trace elements when misused. In a physiological state, the presence of cobalt and manganese traces harmonises the workload of white globules and of the suprarenal gland, also in charge of our defence. Our internal milieu contains about five micrograms of manganese per one hundred millilitres of plasma. Again, the quantity of this element is tiny, despite the important role it occupies in the activity of our enzymes. Whole wheat bread is rich in manganese. Oats, barley, dried vegetables, blueberries, almonds also contain this element.

In addition, manganese is also indispensable to our metallo-enzymes as it catalyses the chemical reactions of the synthesis of protein and anti-body molecules. It participates for instance in the manufacture of cholesterol, a prime ingredient of the cell membrane structure. A deficiency could lead to serious misunderstandings between our lymphocytes and create imbalances and inappropriate reactions vis-à-vis foreign substances. It is likely that it is in this fashion that these mineral elements moderate and correct our biological defence tactics. That is one reason why they are often prescribed in the case of food allergies.

Magnesium

In a healthy subject, magnesium is present in blood plasma in three different forms. Firstly a free form made of positively charged atoms. That is magnesium in an ionic state. It is a positive ion with two positive electric charges, always at the ready to capture two negatively charged electrons in order to relieve the tension, which might prevail in any part of the cell factory.

The second form of blood magnesium is transported by a protein, which delivers it to the cell when needed. The carrier plays the role of a guide rail to enforce a rhythm in the reactions it initiates.

The remainder of the magnesium is retained by complex structures such as the phosphates of our bony tissue. It is from this reserve that the organism draws the mineral matter it requires to function.

An adult body contains about thirty grams of magnesium, of which half is stored in the skeleton, and a quarter in the muscles, which have a pressing need for this metal to operate. When magnesium is in short supply, there can be difficulty with muscular contraction, because a lack of muscle tone in the fibres which form the sheath of the intestinal wall.

We ingest, every day, about three hundred and fifty milligrams of this element, found in cereals, vegetables and dairy products. However, bread containing too much bran has too high a level of phytic acid, and this can block the absorption of magnesium. In this case one should eat more fruit and vegetables. Too much coffee and tea leads to an excessive intake of oxalic acid, which combines with magnesium in a chemical reaction. The resulting compound is an insoluble complex that the intestine can no longer easily absorb. Someone complaining about bloating often believes that a cup of strong coffee can help alleviate his flatulence; the opposite is true. This beverage further impairs magnesium uptake by the intestine and aggravates the condition.

Once its mission is accomplished, magnesium does not hang around the organism. Two thirds of the metal reserves are eliminated through the bowel movements, and the remaining third via the bladder. So we need a constant input to satisfy our daily requirements which supply the vital energy of our cell machinery.

Curiously, magnesium is the only metal whose absorption needs special treatment and this is provided by a specific group of enzymes, coded by a specific programme (of the genes), located on the two chromosomes of the sixth pair: precisely where the repertory of our immunological defence is encoded. This mineral element is thus directly implicated in our defence and nutrition mechanisms. The failure, or the alteration of these genes, provokes the appearance of a congenital disease resulting in the poor absorption of this metal, even if present in the content of the intestine. This genetic disease, fortunately, is quite rare. But it is while studying it that we were better able to understand the symptoms provoked by the deficiency of this element.

On a normal diet, there is, in fact, very little magnesium in the content of the intestine, but it is largely sufficient because our dedicated enzymes locate and capture it immediately. This phenomenon requires an expenditure of energy, which is provided by the metal itself. However, if the magnesium concentration in the food increases, our enzymes do not have to intervene, and absorption occurs passively just through intestinal wall diffusion.

These studies explain why some people frequently suffer from intestinal laziness. It stems from a relative incapacity to pick up enough magnesium from the ingested food. This deficit, often from an enzymatic cause, can result in manifestations of variable intensity, depending on individual constitution and life style. Women are often more affected than men.

Magnesium functions as a sort of pump on the membrane of every cell, helping the cell to extract calcium and sodium. In exchange, it introduces potassium. When the level of magnesium drops, the nerve cell is excited, while the muscle cells go into a trance. Thereafter, cramps and tetany threaten the muscles and perturb the harmonious contraction of the digestive tract. The subject, who is affected in such a way, often complains of having 'a lump in the throat' and difficulty in swallowing. The secretion of digestive glands, indispensable for the absorption of food, then becomes inoperative. A vicious circle begins. Bloating impedes digestion and the lack of magnesium further aggravates intestinal sluggishness.

In severe cases, one has even observed behavioural troubles associated with magnesium deprivation in cells. Some of those affected were misdiagnosed as mental patients, while all they were lacking was a bit of magnesium to nourish the brain. Unexplained tiredness, cardiac palpitations, insomnia, limb tetany, endocrine disorders resulting in irregular and painful periods, have all been recorded under conditions of excessive loss of this mineral element. One must take care to compensate this loss by an additional intake.

More seriously, the loss of magnesium results in an excess of calcium inside the cell, which subjects this living machinery to the risk of calcification. It comes as no surprise to encounter certain auto-immune diseases with rheumatic pain symptoms and a significant deficit in magnesium.

For the digestive tract, with its constant coordinated movements, the slightest shortage of magnesium is unforgiving, as it is the organ in greatest need of it. Stomach cramps, bilious attacks, flatulence, and a heavy feeling in the pelvic and lumbar regions are the most common manifestations. Bladder spasms with an urge to urinate and urine loss can be observed amongst children as well as the aged.

The level of magnesium in the blood is never constant. It varies with the frequency of our meals. In the morning, before food intake, it is at its lowest. That is why gastric cramps and bloating often happen around 11 am. Those who are often prone to these symptoms should always have a good breakfast: that is the best cure.

For the muscle fibre mechanism to function correctly, it needs energy. Practically, no energy production can happen in our cells without the help of magnesium. This metal intervenes in numerous stages of the cellular machinery. It is in charge of activating the work of enzymes, the tireless workers of our body. The magnesium ions carry out this job by stripping electrons and juggling them from one molecule to another. Whether the nutritive substances be sugars, proteins or fats, ionic magnesium is always capable of extracting electrons, and thus energy, to fuel the work of our cells. And it is called upon wherever one needs its spark, able to start up and catalyse the chemical reactions in a given direction. The incredible multiplicity of intervention sites (over three hundred enzymatic systems require it to complete digestion) explain the diversity of manifestations encountered, when it is lacking. Conversely, it helps explain why a little magnesium goes a long way in alleviating many of these symptoms.

Potassium

Potassium is the essential positive ion of the cell factory. In terms of cell reserves it is by far the most important of all mineral elements. There is forty times more potassium in the cells than outside and they jealously guard this precious mineral treasure. They spend it parsimoniously and control inputs and outputs via several pumps, canals and locks located at the level of the membrane. Even its circulation within the cellular factory follows strict rules governing every movement. If our organism takes such care regarding potassium, it must certainly be because it provides indispensable properties for the maintenance of life.

Variations in the blood environment, of course, exert a major influence on the direction of the potassium ions migration. Any loss of liquid by the organism, for instance, is a source of acidosis. Diarrhoea, vomiting, prolonged and high fever, excessive perspiration provoke a loss of water and salts. This loss, in turn, causes the blood environment to turn acid. In this case, potassium leaves the cell to compensate the loss and attempts to re-establish equilibrium. Its departure depletes the cell of its normal store; at a loss, it calls upon hydrogen nuclei (protons with a positive charge) to make up for the precious potassium ions. As a result, the cell is struck by an insurmountable torpor. For the digestive tract this means tiredness and anorexia. To compensate, the only recourse is to supply a modest amount of the missing salt to restart the cellular factory anew.

From a practical viewpoint, these digestive manifestations remain the only obvious signs. Extreme fatigue, loss of reflexes and respiratory difficulty only surface in serious cases when the potassium reserve has become severely depleted. To replenish the store at such an extreme level of deficiency naturally requires an energetic and prolonged treatment that only urgency care can provide. So it is important to address any imbalance in this most vital element of our cells, right from the start. The cells of the heart muscle suffer in the same way as the intestinal muscle cells, while continuing to perform their basic task. Their suffering can usually be detected by anomalies in the electrocardiogram. The concentration of the potassium rate in urine is also a good indicator in suspicious cases. Everything must then be put into action when confronted with a serious deficit of potassium ions, before it starts affecting the cardiac performance.

The quasi-totality of the store of this mineral element (3000 meq) is located in the cells, where it maintains volume and pressure by retaining water molecules. Only 2 per cent of the store circulates within the blood vessels. Potassium is thus the element responsible for the forces which direct the exchange between the cell and the external milieu, supply nutrients and get rid of waste. It is the difference between the ions on either side of the membrane, where they are massed in unequal proportions, which creates the electrical current necessary for the movement of molecules crossing this barrier in one way or another. As there is very little potassium outside, every shortage, however minimal, further aggravates the difference in the energy level: the result, an exacerbated muscle and nerve cell sensitivity. That is the reason why an insignificant loss or an insufficient absorption of this salt causes digestive tract laziness. Conversely, even a minimal compensation allows everything to get back to normal. That explains why the trace of potassium and magnesium provided by a flute of champagne is more than sufficient to stimulate the stomach and bowel movements.

Cholecystokinin

This hormone was discovered, in 1970, by Viktor Mutt, a Swedish biologist. He did not realise, at the time, the important role that this molecule was playing in the peristaltic contractions of the digestive tract. It involved a hormone produced by specialised cells of the intestinal wall. It penetrates the blood stream to modify the muscular structure of the digestive tract, ordering the 'evacuation' of food. It stimulates, furthermore the secretion of the pancreas and liver, as well as that of the small glands in the stomach wall. That is not all; far from it. It has subsequently been discovered that this digestive hormone was also present in the nerve cells of the intestine where it operates like a real chemical messenger, i.e. a neurotransmitter. Then, in 1975, the Belgian biologist J.J. Vanderhaegen found it in the brain.

By injecting this substance into animals one has noted anorexic states, while its presence in trace quantities stimulates food intake. But the usefulness of this multi-faceted molecule goes even further. Numerous regions of the brain produce it and use it to initiate an emotional response. Here we are confronted with an action, both central and peripheral, the effects of which are complementary and self-reinforcing. The arousal of appetite and the initiation of digestion coincide with the enticing desire to take nourishment. Thereafter, cholecystokinin blocks the process as soon as the quantity of absorbed food is judged to be sufficient. We are dealing, in fact, with a double action, intelligent molecule.

Lithium

In the human organism, lithium is mostly concentrated in the nervous system (barely 20 micrograms per 1000 cm3). It behaves like a trace element endowed with an excellent tranquillizing effect on the brain. It would be interesting to understand its mode of action at the level of the nerve cell. The lithium atom is much smaller than either sodium or calcium. Even combined with half a water molecule it only measures three angstroms; this relative scale allows it to easily cross the channels situated in the cell membrane, which have a diameter of five angstroms. Lithium quickly penetrates the cell and fixes itself on many receptor sites, normally reserved for sodium, calcium and other neurotransmitters. This process explains the large number of biological effects it triggers in the cellular factory: lowering of the receptors' sensitivity to neurotransmitters; slowing down in the transport and synthesis systems of the latter; inhibitory effect even on enzymes (as, for instance adenylcyclase, indispensable in the manufacture of the cell fuel); paralysis of certain inhibiting hormones. All these mechanisms explain why champagne sometimes acts so efficiently on melancholic conditions. It has also been put forward as a simple treatment for the prevention of depression as soon as the elusive symptoms, if they manifest themselves, are perceived in the patient. It is surprising, and fascinating, to realise that minimal traces of lithium are capable of deep modifications in such subtle and fleeting conditions as anguish, insomnia or this deep pain that Malraux has painted in pathetic terms in 'The Human Condition': 'Anguish wrenches his stomach... strange sensation, anguish; one can feel by the rhythm of the heart that breathing is poor, as if one breathed through the heart...'

The conventional idea associates the sensitivity of our state of mind with more complex substances, such as tranquillizers. The physico-chemical simplicity of this trace element raises the hope that someday we may be able to understand the capriciousness of our 'mood'.

Recent work in neurobiology has shown that lesions artificially created in certain specific zones of the rat brain immediately induce a mood of indifference; the animal is incapable of vigilance and adequate reactions in the face of danger. So there is a functional deficiency directly related to a behavioural anomaly. This has been confirmed by the technique of ideography, associated with the injection of sugar marked with radio-active carbon. This allows the visualisation of each part of the brain on a screen. In a normal man, the anterior zone of the brain consumes a large amount of sugar. This particular activity of the frontal lobe results in the display of red and orange colours in a brain image. On the other hand, subjects in a depressive state reveal either a noticeable decrease, or an inordinate increase in sugar consumption, which shows up in different colours. These mood crises might stem from a functional deficiency of the frontal lobe or from the deep layers of the brain, provoked by an imbalance of the chemical substances secreted by neurones.

The role of neurotransmitters in depressive states: Dopamine

We know that our nerve cells converse by releasing chemical substances called neurotransmitters. One of them, dopamine, is released at the very end of the tenuous ramifications of the nerve cell (dendrite). This discharge does not just happen randomly, it is harmoniously adapted, in rhythm and quantity, according to the need for a response and the intensity of the environment stimuli. A disorderly release of dopamine, by excess or default, too brief or too long, risks shocking the delicacy of the neighbouring cell and thereby rupture the harmony of the system. Such disorders may well be at the source of inadequate behaviour. It also explains why champagne sometimes delivers a delicious sensation of well-being. It intervenes by stimulating the discharge of dopamine while adding its own property, which mimics the effect of the neurotransmitter. In such an event, the patient sees dark thoughts vanish as if by magic. Conversely, if the subject suffers from a dopamine overdose, this remedy will not only be inoperative, but also exacerbate the depression.

The dopamine molecule, once secreted, will be captured by a negative mould (receptor), located on the filament of a neighbouring nerve cell. This physical contact between dopamine and its receptor induces a micro-electric current, which will switch its neighbour in turn to transmit the message to code and decode. Here again, the quantity and efficiency of the receptors condition the intensity of the organism reaction.

Each of us is genetically programmed to produce a greater or lesser quantity of receptors endowed with an individual capacity. As such, some subjects react violently, some indifferently, to the same situation. Neither sedatives, nor champagne for that matter, can do anything about the nature and the number of these receptors, since they depend on genetic factors, but they substantially modify the other neurotransmitters and thus act, indirectly, to bring about alterations in mood one way or another. This highly complex process is behind the randomness of observed effects. Sometimes, relief is obtained, when one was expecting the worst, after a single sip of wine; sometimes it is the opposite.

Let us keep up with the work of this dopamine. After completing its mission to relay the message to the neighbouring cell, specialised workers spring into action; these are enzymes charged with the quick destruction of the dopamine or any other neurotransmitter, as a nerve cell can equally release several neurotransmitters of a different nature and function! So everyone must work according to a precise and synchronised programme, orchestrated by the indispensable enzymes, which also help the first nerve cell recover some of the neurotransmitters released. A reminder that our organism is both simultaneously efficient and frugal.

It may just so happen that enzymes may be insufficient, indifferent or incompetent in their mission; dopamine is then neither destroyed nor recovered. In this case the persistence or excess, of dopamine, or of any other transitory messenger substance (serotonin, acetylcholine...) tends to accumulate in the gap (or synapse) separating two neurones. This surplus continues to excite the next cell, thus provoking other aberrant messages; a source of unusual symptoms (exhaustion, indifference, incoherence...).

Certain drugs (amphetamines, imipramine...) increase the dopamine discharge. They can then trigger a depression even in healthy subjects. Certain neuroleptics are prescribed to help eliminate excess dopamine, which explains their therapeutic effect. Unfortunately, dopamine accumulation is not the only phenomenon responsible for depression; a number of other neurotransmitters (serotonin, phenyethyamine...) are also trapped in the deep zones of the brain. Their unwelcome presence is signalled by an abnormal concentration in the cerebrospinal liquid bathing the nervous system. The same goes for nor-adrenaline and certain morphin-like substances of the brain.

The complexity of the neurotransmitters with a contradictory action, partially explains the spectacular relief sometimes recorded after a modest intake of champagne. Indeed, certain enzymes could be spurred, under the exhilarating influence of the wine, to a renewed level of enthusiasm in the performance of their task, either by quickly annihilating the surplus hormones, or by hastening their recapture by the mother-cell which initially secreted them; it could also turnout differently. It is well understood that this natural remedy cannot deliver a consistent result, as everything depends on the result of the complex reactions between the various chemical messengers. In general, champagne initiates, after five to six minutes, a quick and ample discharge of neurotransmitters; the brain cells then progressively empty their chemical store and their enzymes. It is during this phase, lasting two to three hours, that a sensation of joyful buoyancy permeates the soul and flushes away the state of anguish. Well, in most cases.

Zinc

Each atom of zinc carries a positive charge (Zn^+) incorporated in several families of metallo-enzymes. One of them is represented by the indispensable neutral endopeptidase, a zinc enzyme the function of which is to degrade some enkephalines which maintain vigilance. By supplying ionic zinc one allows this enzyme to buid up the reserve, and increase its efficiency in preparing the brain to prepare for the initial phase of sleep. That explains why a short cure of a week or two is amply sufficient to regain a normal sleep pattern, without the need to swallow pills to fall asleep or wake up. In reality, our nerve and glandular cells need very few zinc ions to regulate the rhythm of their activity.

It would be of interest to better understand the importance of ionic zinc, the presence of which is necessary to maintain the harmony prevailing amongst the various chemical messengers operating in the brain.

There is as much zinc as iron in our body, with both metals in balance; they also react synergistically to allow electrons to jump from one molecule to another while producing energy at a moderate tempo. Zinc is especially concentrated in the endocrine glands and at the base of the brain, in the hypothalamo-hypopheasal complex. This lower level of the brain functions as a set of glands secreting a variety of hormones.

Nearly four-fifths of the enzymes of our organism contain zinc ions. The metal is thus a prime ingredient in all of the biochemical reactions of our cells. Our daily food intake supplies roughly 10 mg of zinc. A variety of foodstuff is rich in zinc: cereals, fruits, yeasts, mushrooms, meat...without forgetting champagne. The muscle fibres in the blood vessel wall are the ones with the highest concentration. Nearly all the enzymes, which perform around the cell nucleus, contain the metal. Gross variations in content have a direct impact on cell performance.

It is possible to induce a sharp zinc deficiency in an experimental animal, which results in many digestive, skin and blood related disturbances. We do not know if the animal suffers from insomnia. Epidemiologists have observed children suffering from severe malnutrition, leading to growth retardation, in Egypt and Iran. These children present a characteristic deficit of zinc and enzymes. Subsequent zinc treatment has permitted a recovery in their stature, but insomnia was not detected amongst them. On the other hand, in the case of digestive troubles, with poor chronic food absorption, the zinc content falls significantly. It is amongst this second group of patients that insomnia and headaches are frequent symptoms. They respond well to zinc administration.

As a trace element, its toxicity is certain when the ingested food contains an excessive dose. In industry, the inhalation of fumes containing traces of zinc is regarded as a work-related accident. In these two cases, its toxicity manifests itself by intense digestive trouble, headaches and insomnia.

Neurotransmitters and the mystery of sleep: Serotonin

In spite of the great progress made in neurobiology, sleep is a state which is incredibly difficult to grasp. That is because there is no known dedicated structure or function, at least for the time being, for this nocturnal rest. We still do not know what sleep is for, how it comes about and yet 20 to 25 per cent of the population suffers from sleep problems. Everybody realises that sleep is essential for the maintenance of physical and mental health. It is a major scientific challenge. One can fall asleep in different circumstances: boredom, tiredness, lack of interest, lack of stimulation, heat, cold, satiety, prolonged waking, after tender moments... but none of these circumstances can trigger sleep on its own. While there is an organ to see, another to hear, there is no sleep centre. On the contrary it requires several complex systems acting synergistically and with functional synchronicity to trigger sleep. Then, the whole being participates in order to maintain it. Torpor may arise suddenly and invade the organism; meanwhile the brain undergoes electrical storms and stimulates its chemical reactions in the mist of dreams. The disproportion and asynchronicity of the biological phenomena involved, in time and space, and in their intensity, is most disconcerting.

Our central nervous system, despite its strength, remains an extremely sensitive organ when confronted with a brutal change in the sleep/wake cycle. It is always the first to react and suffer.

Curiously, of all the species studied, mankind is the only one to conserve its bio-rythm over a fairly lengthy period. Rats, birds and cats, subjected to an artificial change in lighting, adapt their sleep pattern to the imposed conditions. Their system of adaptation seems more dependent on the environment. Man, a socio-cultural animal, attaches little importance to the physical conditions of the milieu (light, sun movements, temperature); what matters most for him are the socio-cultural signals which provide him with the benchmarks to synchronise his internal rhythm: life style, working hours. He can, to a certain extent, free himself from sidereal time and replace it with an artificial time of his own. For many, alas, it is the subway time table which imposes the rhythm of rest and work. Paradoxically, it is the constraints of social life, which dictate their cadence, to which our internal clocks are set, more or less happily, as everybody needs enough sleep to match their temperament. This extends from five to twelve hours in extreme cases. Everybody has a certain sleep pattern. It is even genetically programmed on the sixth pair of our chromosomes, where our genetic identity is also inscribed. Biologically speaking, the future does not necessarily belong to those who get up early...

Against the most elementary rules of nature, could it be that man is the only animal who can emancipate himself from the alternation of day and night, thanks to his socio-cultural organisation? Our biological clocks do indeed operate in a much more complex fashion than for animals. The most studied example is the secretion of melatonin, a chemical messenger elaborated by the epiphysis under the stimulation of light. This hormone obeys the alternating cycle of sleep/wakefulness. It is during the night that melatonin is discharged to slow down the activity of the hypothalamus centres, thus decreasing their hormonal secretion. In the induction of the sleep mode, melatonin also intervenes in a cyclic mode, by setting a rhythm to the operation of the sleep circuits, of temperature and muscle tone. This mission requires the co-operation of certain trace elements like copper and iron. The copper participates in the release of nor-adrenaline, while iron is needed in the synthesis of dopamine. It is these two neurotransmitters, which help the epiphysis to produce melatonin during the day. A shortage of these metals in an ionic state leads to a drop in melatonin and thereby to a more difficult induction of sleep.

Unknowingly, someone who drinks half a glass of champagne instead of taking a sleeping pill absorbs 6 mg of ionic copper and 0,05 mg of iron. The mineral elements help to correct indirectly the imbalance of the glands and nerve cells. They also activate the enzymes in the regulation of the neurotransmitters (serotonin, gamma-amino-butyric acid or GABA), which slow down the centres of wakefulness.

Certain complex alcohols, such as pentanols, hexanols and propanols, possess the capacity to encourage the secretion of neurotransmitters in the deepest layers of the brain (locus cerulus), which are responsible for the onset of sleep.

Serotonin, for instance, frequently involved during a depressive bout, induces behavioural indifference and somnolence. The potency of this neurotransmitter varies quickly depending on the nature of the food absorbed but that is only the case in specific types.

From a biochemical point of view, serotonin derives from its raw material, tryptophane, one of the protein amino acids. To consume a lot of meat does not result necessarily in an excess of serotonin, as the other amino acids harmoniously balance its concentration in the brain. On the other hand, a sugar-rich diet induces an important release of insulin, which in turn triggers an increase of tryptophane, and serotonin, thus facilitating the penetration of the barrier which protects the brain against foreign substances.

Normally, there is an alternating balance between the state of wakefulness and sleep. The operation of these two systems is underpinned by complex mechanisms, which call upon more or less specialised nerve centres with their arsenal of chemical substances and electric waves. Acetylcholine and certain endorphins, for instance, play a primary role in the state of wakefulness by stimulating nerve networks situated beneath the cortex. Nor-adrenalin, another neurotransmitter of this brain alchemy, exerts its action on certain deep formations of the central nervous system to induce somnolence and sleep. Other categories of chemical messengers of our nerve cells (serotonin, dopamine) also participate in the alternation between wakefulness and sleep. There is no single specific substance, which is responsible for sleep as such, nor for being awake; but rather a whole array of various molecules, the nuances in the proportions of which, induce either vigilance, or sleep and dreams. The same chemical substances are present everywhere during wakefulness as well as during dreams. Everything rests on their nuances and mysterious interactions in the brain circuitry.

The role of neurotransmitters in migraine

Amongst the fast-acting neurotransmitters, we are familiar with acetylcholine and such amino acids in the form of glutamate and aspartate (glutamate is frequently used in many industrial foods to enhance flavour). These molecules exert an exciting action. Acetylcholine, for instance, abruptly expands the calibre of vessels. Normally, it is immediately neutralised by enzymes, once its mission accomplished, to limit its activity. A deficiency in enzymatic control can prolong the acetylcholine effect up to the point of disrupting system harmony. Certain forms of migraine, with facial and back flush, are caused by this type of mechanism. Medical treatment is then required. Wine ingestion only aggravates vessel dilatation and thus migraine. The indication for each remedy is precise, given the variety of possible causes. There is no standard treatment applicable to all.

Slow-acting neurotransmitters function like hormones. It is the case for catecholamines (adrenaline, nor-adrenaline, dopamine) and serotonin. These chemical messengers activate the ions (calcium, phosphorus, energy molecules) present in the cell factory. Under these conditions, catecholamines act to constrict the vessels. In this case one needs to use drugs capable of blocking their action. Beta-blockers are remarkable for that purpose. The medicine used in this case acts in reverse fashion to those involved in fighting vascular dilatation, where ergotamine extracts are better indicated.

Nature is full of surprises. Many substances secreted in the brain can have two diametrically opposed actions! Acetylcholine, for instance, released by a nerve cell of the parasympathetic system can induce a brief (1/1000 of a second) excitation to open the ionic channels of the neurones, while also imposing a long-term state of stimulation lasting several minutes. How does it manage such a feat? Acetylcholine acts on two different receptors: a fast-acting one, located in the channels where calcium and potassium ions transit; a slow-acting one activating the cellular factory machinery. Thus the final effect does not rest entirely on the nature of the neurotransmitter but also on the receptor. It is this second molecule, made out of proteins, which decides on the length and modality of action. This information is of great practical importance. It would be much more logical, for a remedy to act on the receptor, by blocking it, for instance, to obtain a specific result. And that is exactly what medicine has managed to achieve in the case of catecholamines when implicated in migraine. These neurotransmitters possess up to three different receptors: alpha 1 and alpha 2, and a third one named beta. The doctor seeks to block beta with a synthetic molecule, which resembles a catecholamine. The receptor is fooled and remains inactive, incapable of releasing the slightest energy to prompt the cellular machinery. This molecular impersonation prevents the real catecholamines from kicking into action, with receptors already saturated by the intruders. As a result, the narrowing of vessels, provoked by catecholamines, which lead to the contraction of the muscle fibres lining the artery walls, is reduced. However, not all migraines respond to this type of treatment; only about 60 per cent respond to this therapy. And, strangely enough, the effect diminishes over time, as if the receptors had discovered the trick and were no longer fooled by it.

Our brain is also equipped with modulating systems in all cells. Their mission is to slow or encourage the neurotransmitters' action depending on the circumstances. They can modify the programme of several opposing effect systems in order to harmonise the operation of the whole. The intestinal vaso-active polypeptide (VIP) is a protein molecule playing the role of an enzyme. It is secreted in the digestive tract and nerve cells. One of the roles played in the brain consists of regulating the functioning of cells as well as local circulation. It is an important relaxation system, capable of reducing the muscle cell contraction of artery walls. Any imbalance may well be implicated in the build-up of migraine.

We know that VIP, as a digestive enzyme, is abundantly released in the digestive tract and even more so after absorption of a glass of champagne. Could this substance reach the central nervous system to relax vessel spasms in a crisis? It seems not. The occasional beneficial effect of the wine is more likely to come from the localised discharge of synthesised VIP by certain nerve clusters. They empty their reserves. And that explains why a second glass of champagne is often ineffective.

Another molecule, substance P, also intervenes as a regulating agent of nerve circuits, especially in cases of distress or pain. It helps to control the secretion of acetylcholine and nor-adrenaline. It is likely that lack of control in its release flow is behind certain types of migraine.

In some, the release of this type of molecule is increased by champagne, while in others it is the reverse. The lack of consistency of our ancestral remedy may come from this wide variance.

Somostatine, which is generated simultaneously, amplifies the tone of muscle cells. It is suspected to play a role in the slow onset of this affliction.

The existence of such a complex arsenal of chemical substances and receptors shows that our nerve circuitry is under constant surveillance, correction, adjustment, activation, slow down, modification, modulation. They all aim at balancing and harmonising the various functions. The greater the complexity of our cerebral organisation, the more the cells, which make it up, must scrupulously respect the team's operational code. There is a need for constant dialogue, contact maintenance, sending and receiving highly specific chemical and electrical messages, in order to be permanently informed about changes in the internal and external environments. That is why it is necessary to be able to understand the various levels of the central nervous system if one wants to penetrate the arcane world of migraine. From the physiological level of the brain, in its relationship with other organs, to the level of cellular and molecular biology, discrete interactions are everywhere in evidence. The slightest modification in one area impacts on the others. The infinite nuances in the range of functioning, far from confusing us, offer, actually a wide array of operational choice to the organism. Modern medicine can now intervene on different facets of these diverse systems, in order to obtain a certain degree of control, and to shift reactions towards the desired goal. All of this becomes possible thanks to the knowledge of the brain which rules us.

We do know that the brain is not made up simply of neurones. Each cellular unit is meticulously protected by an army of glial cells to help and support. In a way, a neurone is like a lord with his retinue of servants and soldiers. That is why there are many more glial cells in the brain than neurones. Glial cells are of two types: astrocytes, which look like sea urchins bristling with spikes connecting all nerve elements; oligodendrocytes, equally covered with tentacles. Like neurones, glial cells are able to secrete chemical substances and send electrical messages to communicate with their master. It is thanks to their devotion that the neurone is able to accomplish its task. Although we do not yet understand the real meaning of these conversations, we know that some raw materials are first sifted through by these protective cells and then extensively prepared before delivery to the neurones, which in turn transform them into neurotransmitters. Waste is also recovered by the glial cells for recycling. This happens, we believe, through the coding of the electrical messages between the elements of the circuit. It seems clear that any functional disturbance in the operation of these indispensable protective cells is behind many a migraine. Possibly, they may fail to properly execute their cleansing or watch function, leaving undesirable molecules to accumulate and put pressure on the neurone.

Some remedies intervene at this level to stimulate the enzymatic apparatus. That is what happens with champagne, which can sometimes nip an incipient migraine.

The contribution of incremental energetic substances, notably complex sugars, could activate the enzymes charged with the balanced nutrition of the brain.

Recently, thanks to the technique of fluorescence, it has became possible to highlight the presence of communication channels (or gap-junctions) between neurones and glial cells, undeniable proof of the intimate relations between master and servants, caught in the midst of chemical conversations. Neurobiologists have even discovered that each of these discrete cells is charged with its own specificity, a sort of personality, to perform several particular functions for the neurone to which it is attached. The neurone, although a noble cell, only communicates via monotonous waves with almost identical oscillations. On the contrary, the glial cells are much more talkative; their electrical signals are not only varied, but each glial cell has its own style, while all neurones speak in the same tonality. The individuality of these protective cells has perplexed researchers. Some are able to emit electric frequencies similar to those of the heart. They appear like microscopic beats, each beating according to their own rhythm. We have no idea about the exact meaning of this concert. To use an analogy, it would seem that the neurones sing in unison, while the servants improvise, each according to its own inspiration. And it is exactly these exaggerations or fantasies which one notices amongst them in the case of migraine. Certain wines, especially red, even encourage the debauchery of the glial cells and, as a derivative effect, will induce migraine.

These devoted cells, charged with protecting their masters, guard them jealously. Their membrane, adhering to the neurone membrane, is pierced with intermittently opening and nearly invisible channels. This system of locks allows the periodic passage of neurotransmitters and nutrients from the glial cell to the neurone and vice versa. It is through these controllable gap-junctions that they communicate. As this system is very tenuous it is possible that any deficiency in the valves can momentarily disrupt the supply of the neurones, hence their hunger and panic. The membrane of these protective cells consumes potassium in positive ionic form voraciously. This supply ensures stabilisation of the potassium level in the cerebrospinal liquid in which the brain bathes.

They control at the same time the balance between the other ions such as calcium, magnesium, phosphorus, which are responsible for neurone vitality and emission of electrical waves.

Flavonoids

How do flavonoids act during the onset of migraine? In a person who does not drink any wine other than champagne, flavonoids, normally present, first destroy certain enzymes charged with the neutralisation of the toxic phenols of the wine. This leads to the unfortunate passage of these unwanted phenols into the bloodstream. These substances cannot, of course, reach the cerebral tissue itself, since the permanent capillary barrier of the brain (the hemato-encephalic barrier) stands guard. But their presence in the bloodstream irritates the internal wall of the cerebral vessels. Covered with endothelial cells, these are particularly sensitive to these disturbances, opening the possibility of a crisis should the enzymes fail to eliminate the intruders.

The experiment was undertaken at The Queen Charlotte Hospital in London, under the direction of Professor Merton Sandler. It was initially thought that it was the ethyl alcohol which was responsible for the headaches in subjects prone to migraine, who could not tolerate wine. The team, which performed the experiment, had the idea to split the migraine sufferers in several groups, given either wine or pure alcohol, or flavonoids only.

They were surprised to find that only those drinking wine or a solution of flavonoids complained of headaches, while pure ethanol did not provoke any reaction, neither did the presence of tyramine. The end result is that people subject to migraine should know that nearly all wines should be avoided, with the exception of champagne, with a very low flavonoid content; they can also enjoy, if they can afford it, good quality wines aged in casks or sold 'on the lees'.

Lipoproteins

Fatty cells are surprisingly sensitive to many hormones. They even constitute a reserve bank where they are stored. Under these conditions, the stimulated cells place in reserve a significant quantity of nutritive substances and their girth expands. This mechanism in turn encourages the appetite and leads to a risk of overeating. For this reason, a regular weight check-up is advisable when on the pill. The same goes for dietary cautions concerning the abuse of certain fats, sugared drinks and pastries.

In the organism, the ingested food is first absorbed, after digestion, in the intestine. There it is transformed into droplets of chylomicron, made of proteins and fat, to be processed further by enzymes from the liver cells. The nutritive substances are then loaded in small 'delivery vans', very low-density lipoprotein molecules (VLDL), which have as their mission to distribute them across all the blood vessels, and especially to the muscles and fatty tissues. There, a second category of factories, also equipped with enzymes, crush them again and reduce them to elementary units. These capillary factories also generate energy.

As our organism is essentially thrifty, it recovers a lot and hates waste. Thus there is an enormous amount of material to transport through the bloodstream. These are the heavy-duty trucks, the high-density lipoproteins (HDL), which are in charge of picking up all deliveries. Under normal conditions there is a balance in the traffic of these various transport vehicles, which are only lipoprotein molecules. If there are too many small vans (VLDL) on the small roads of the blood network, they will hinder the activity of the heavy trucks (HDL). The resulting traffic jam lies behind the thickening of the arterial wall. Certain hormones (the oestrogen of certain pills) and excessive fat in food increase the enzymatic activity of the liver. Many VLDL vans, loaded with nutrients, leave the hepatic factory and create a jam in the blood circulation. One can detect these traffic jams by the dosage of the level of triglycerides in plasma. A rise in this complex fat signals an excess of low-density lipoproteins. Depending on the subjects, the increase can vary between 20 to 80 per cent over the norm. However, four out of five individuals do not react in the same fashion faced with the same trigger factors (food excess, the pill, tobacco, alcohol): there is, without doubt, an individual predisposition to react intensely through an inadequate production of lipoproteins.

Certain subjects do not have enough receptors on the surface of their cells to capture the lipoproteins. As a consequence, they cannot penetrate the cells where they are supposed to be broken down by enzymes. The lipoproteins accumulate in the bloodstream and tend to deposit in the arterial walls. Other individuals present deficient enzymatic equipment and show themselves incapable of converting their fat reserves into energy quickly. In such a situation, the thrifty cells end up hypertrophying and thickening the adipose tissue.

Valves are also positioned along the luminal wall of the capillaries. Their role is to prevent a counter flow of the liquid. This exhausting task requires a support system. The endothelial cells of the lymphathic ducts are anchored to the collagen fibres of the skin and benefit automatically from the pumping of the lymph. This liquid must never stagnate. Every hour, over twenty litres of lymph, spread over a surface of one thousand square metres, are filtered in this manner. The flow must be fast, as each cubic centimetre of lymph can only stay in the same spot for three seconds.

Beyond that, there is the risk of a bottleneck with undesirable deposits of large molecules of lipoproteins. The lymphatic river, which irrigates the skin, runs at an amazing speed. It must renew all the time not only in order to perform efficient drainage of the skin, but also to supply nutrition and remove waste. If a miniscule vein becomes clogged, the pressure downstream increases immediately in the neighbouring capillaries, the local flow becomes insufficient, and a danger of stagnation and deposits arises.

All our cells bathe in this thick liquid derived from blood plasma. It is incredibly important; lymph (or the interstitial liquid) represents about 15 per cent of the body weight. It is truly in this liquid, our 'internal milieu', in the expression of Claude Bernard, that the exchange of cells with the ambient environment takes place to allow nutrition, breathing and detoxification. After having accomplished its mission, lymph filters through the capillaries' wall and is again caught by the flow of the veinous circulation.

To activate the progress of this lymphatic flow, the wall of these tenuous vessels is equipped with contractile molecules (actin, myosin, tubulin), which pump the interstitial liquid in a rhythmic fashion. The contraction is strongly stimulated by the supply of energy and ionic minerals. This phenomenon explains why champagne is often helpful in the activation of lymphatic circulation by eliminating waste in the tissues.

The dietetic quality of wine increases the beneficial concentration of certain high-density lipoproteins (HDL 3), which contributes in lowering the degree of low-density lipoproteins (LDL), clogging traffic and tending to deposit as soon as they are in excess.

The biology of desire

Injected in infinitesimal doses in an animal, gonadoliberin immediately induces a receptive attitude vis-a-vis a sexual partner. Strangely, many impotence and frigidity treatments using this 'luteinizing release hormone' in the ovaries often fail. This shows that the hormone is not acting on its own. The biology of desire is in fact the result of a confluence of many factors, mixing biology and culture, romance and poetry, tenderness and love. Everything surprises when one studies the mystery of love as each factor can influence sexuality, one way or the other. Personality and education also impinge on the adopted strategy. Although the hormonal factor awakens the nerve centres of passion, it does not play the preponderant role, given the psychological and socio-cultural pressures specific to humankind. In certain cases, poorly dosed or unbalanced hormones even slow the nerve circuits and create inhibition. More often than not, an excess of hormones debilitates love rather than enhances it. At any rate, their influence remains well below the magic that a romantic ambiance creates. There is a hormonal influence on sexual behaviour, but its ambiguity does not permit an objective discrete analysis from the other elements of the sentimental and cultural context. As Claudel said: 'Even intelligence can only fully function under the impulse of desire'.

In normal circumstances, as we saw before, the hormonal secretion of the brain follows precise and programmed rhythms, conditioned by the cyclical alternation of wakefulness and sleep. This diurnal rhythm regulates the activity of the glands and of the central nervous system. That explains how most of our physiological and psychological functions follow the course of time and seasons. For human beings, the best brain performances (memory, vigilance, learning), muscular and motor activities, faculties of adaptation and defence reactions are at their peak in the morning. Other hormones are released around midnight: the growth hormone for instance, while cortisol is discharged by the suprarenal glands mostly at wake-up time. To ensure the rhythm of these diverse cycles, there are several biological clocks - pacemakers - to beat time. Their mission is to regulate these cycles according to a twenty-four hour period (circadian cycle). There is not a single internal clock as previously thought, but several. Evolution has provided us with several coordinated oscillating systems, where lower animals only have one. The location of some of them is relatively well-known following the famous work of Alain Reinberg. At the base of the brain there are at least two: the supra-chiasmatic nodes, which direct the secretion rhythm of the hypothalamic hormones (LH-RH, CRH, TRh) and the arched nodes in charge of releasing other hormones. The epiphysis, a small gland suspended at the top of the central cavity of the brain, also functions like an oscillator serving to regulate the discharge of the light-sensitive hormone, melatonin. Descartes thought it was the 'seat of the soul'. The surface of the brain, the cortex, and more precisely its anterior part, responsible for consciousness and superior faculties (such as programming) also hide several biological clocks timing our daily activities.

In general, the genetic equipment of each individual determines these cyclical functions. Each animal and plant species has its own cadenza. Every day, our organism must set its different clocks in order for the whole to be in synchronous harmony. To that end it gets its cues from the environment (luminosity, noise, temperature), and also the work schedule and the indispensable alarm clock, which puts an end to our sleep. All these environmental signals are necessary references to synchronise our internal clocks and help us unconsciously to adapt to the variations of our milieu.

' There is a time for everything on earth...
A time to love and a time to harvest.'
(Ecclesiastes 3)

If an individual finds himself confined, as an experiment, in a room without any communication with the external environment, his biological rhythms will continue to function, but will progressively extend to over thirty hours instead of twenty-four. It is a sort of internal clock drift, a disorderliness, which varies with individuals. It is natural for the organism to feel the need to set the clock on a daily basis. If the experiment is pursued, the deprived individual will experience a total breakdown in the regular functioning of his organs. Each one will behave independently from the whole and harmony collapses; incoherence sets in. At that stage serious troubles creep in, such as insomnia, lassitude, confusion, anguish, depression. It goes without saying that sentimental or sexual predisposition are severely affected. Those who work night shifts over a long period suffer from a significant disorder in their biological cycle. Some lose total interest in their sexual behaviour. After an adequate period of rest, the biological rhythm becomes normal again and reawakens their natural erotic impulses.

Ovular pains

Nowadays, we know that menstrual blood is not ordinary, as it does not coagulate normally. The periods last from three to eight days. The amount of blood lost during each period varies from twenty to eighty millilitres. As our red globules contain iron, it is conceivable that an exaggerated loss over time could provoke anaemia, if it is not compensated by a balanced dietary contribution. During the first periods, there are many young girls who do not undergo ovulation, their basal temperature taken in bed does not increase and does not go beyond 37 degrees during the second half of the cycle: they are called 'anovular' cycles. Then, after a while, ovulation becomes normal and is followed by the formation of the corpus luteum after egg maturation. During menopause, at the onset, irregular periods are also associated with the absence of ovulation.

The minutely orchestrated concert of feminine hormones explains that any shortfall can often provoke problems and pains during the menstrual cycle. Some pains, for instance, arise two weeks after the first day of the periods and come back every month. This symptom is known as 'ovular pains'. How to explain this phenomenon? In general, it is a dull pain in the lower abdomen, which appears in the middle of the cycle. It coincides with a drop in temperature to about 36 degrees taken in the morning in bed. This temporary drop of the basal temperature is due to the release of certain substances in the follicle containing the egg. It results in a slow-down of urea elimination in the kidneys. Enzymes destroy urea retained (or reabsorbed), which unfortunately yields even more toxic waste (cyanates and ammonium). This, in turn, acts rapidly on the brain by reducing oxygen consumption. Confronted with this situation, the thermostatic centres, located at the base of the brain, are temporarily slowed down. They reduce temperature from about 37.2 to 36.6 degrees. It is a short-term phenomenon, as the kidneys react and eliminate the undesirable waste. It has been reproduced in animals by injections of urea or derivatives. One has even been able to trace the evolution of the urea level in the blood, and temperature before and after ovulation. These experiments are of great practical interest.

The slight morning temperature drop is both a simple and precise signal of ovulation, the time when fertility is optimal. So, if one absorbs a little champagne on the eve, it frequently helps to avoid the unpleasant pelvic pains of ovulation. The wine stimulates both blood circulation and hormonal release, while encouraging renal elimination.

For those who fear repetition of this discomfort, the pain usually lasts about one day only, or slightly longer. Sometimes it is on the right side, sometimes on the left. And at other times it is in the lower abdomen or back. In general, clinical examination is normal. The causes of the pain vary. It might be due to a sudden distension of the follicle containing the egg, which is gorging itself with liquid, but cannot break apart to free the impatient ovum. This happens quite often, following an insufficiency of the hormone of the pituitary gland, (LH or luteotrophic hormone), which helps to mature egg and follicle. In this case, champagne helps to encourage hormonal secretion.

However, the pain could also come from a cystic or fibrous ovary. Obviously champagne cannot remedy sick or poorly formed ovaries. It is not a panacea for all conditions and that explains why many women are disappointed, while others are content with this therapy. In the former case, a full gynaecological examination is necessary to determine whether a structural or functional anomaly of the suspected ovary is the cause of the problem.

Ovulation pain could also come from the liquid contained in the follicle, when the egg has already been released. This nourishing liquid floods the pelvic cavity and irritates the membrane (peritoneum) which covers it. The numerous enzymes present in the liquid are the cause of pain. However, a painful crisis in a subject who until then has never suffered from ovulation, has to be apprehended with suspicion. A medical check-up is advised to determine the specific cause of the symptom. To continue with champagne in this condition, be it with the most expensive, would be foolish, as it might well be the onstart of appendicitis (especially if the pain is located on the right side), lurking salpingitis or exceptionally, an unsuspected extra-uterine pregnancy. It goes without saying that intercourse, under these conditions, would worsen further, even an innocent ovular pain.

Some women, prior to indisposition, present a swelling of ankles, headache, congestion of the lower abdomen and chest, sometimes with acne spots or marks of redness. They are called the 'premenstrual syndrome'. They last from between two to six days before the beginning of the periods and stop fairly quickly with menstruation. Some experience pain in the breasts, pelvis or lower back. Irritability, or the 'blues' can accompany these indispositions with an intensity varying from person to person, and even from cycle to cycle. These were the very symptoms that champagne was called upon to alleviate.

During their periods, women sometimes feel a small abdominal pain. It can wake them up with a sharp release of hormones during sleep. The feeling of heaviness is caused by the contraction of the muscle fibres of the uterus, which slacken and expulse the superficial layer covering the cavity. In most cases there is no noticeable organic cause. It would seem, in light of the research done, to come from an excess of prostaglandins, the local hormones, which stimulate the contraction of the uterus and sensitise it. In general, rest and topical warmth (our grannies' hot water bottle) are adequate remedies. For more severe cases, there are medicines, which neutralise the action of prostaglandins. For instance aspirin and indomethacin, but they have some undesirable side effects. Aspirin encourages blood flow and makes for abundant menses, while indomethacin irritates the stomach and induces vertigo when poorly tolerated. A flute of sparkling champagne is a milder prescription and often as efficient. The calcium and potassium ions it contributes, help harmonise the contraction of the uterine muscle fibres.

Folic Acids

Wine is rich in zinc, the fundamental element of the metallo-enzymes, which participate in the synthesis of glandular hormones. Well-endowed in this trace element, champagne is effective in co-ordinating the hormonal interactions between the various parts of the organism.

The secret of champagne lies in the combination of the trio, zinc-copper-manganese, present in trace amounts. These metals behave as first-rate biocatalytic stimulants of the internal glands. As carriers of electrons, thus energy, their contribution is of prime interest in all endocrine troubles. Their action is especially interesting in cases of hormonal insufficiency. Vitamins (notably folic acid) and higher alcohols largely amplify the trace element's action.

Recent discoveries about this vitamin group, composed of folic acid, have shown that it plays an important role in the functioning of the nerve cells secreting hormones, such as the pituitary gland. These vitamins are synthesised by the vine leaves and by the wine yeasts during aging. In champagne, for instance, there are up to eleven varieties of folic acids, amongst which the most active are di- and tetra-hydrofolates.

The concentration of these acids is much higher in the cerebrospinal fluid than in plasma. As soon as they are absorbed, the precious vitamins are immediately captured by the intestinal wall. They quickly cross the protective barriers of the brain and reach the nerve cells which are equipped with special pumps to catch them. This whole biological setup underscores the importance of their role in the activity of the brain and the glands, Their presence is indispensable for the synthesis of enzymes and hormones based on molecules and proteins. Their participation is absolutely necessary in the build-up of the command structure of the cell (nucleic acids of the nucleus), where memory dictating the synthesis, as well as cyclical activity of the hormones is stored.

In parallel, neurones stimulated by the molecules of higher alcohols release a precise quantity (quantum) of neurotransmitters serving to impart order to the whole system. As a matter of fact, the language of the nerve cells resembles to a certain extent the binary language of computers. Our brain, however, conserves its functional flexibility and adaptability to react to the influences exerted by environmental factors or the internal milieu. It is in this sense that one can hope to alter its activities by supplying it with the elements required by its needs.

In small doses, naturally, there is an undeniable therapeutic effect from champagne bringing harmony to the circuits controlling the various parts of the organism.

The keystone of this astonishing influence resides in the complex organization of the membrane of the nerve and gland cells. The brain behaves effectively like an enormous gland - secreting hormones. The fluidity of the cellular membrane of the brain improves and ensures an optimal and selective exchange between the cell and the outside milieu. The ionic channels also operate efficiently, allowing them to quickly generate electric waves, which underpin information to coordinate the activity of the whole. All of this supposes that the enzymes, which make up this structure, find themselves in the best possible conditions to fulfil their delicate mission. On the contrary, when the dose of wine consumed becomes excessive, the alteration of the membrane happens immediately, although the brain is equipped with the means to rid itself of toxic substances. The fluidity of the cellular membrane diminishes as a result of the stoppages provoked by the excess alcohol. The latter cuts the complex fat molecules (phospholipids), while altering the fatty acids and cholesterol, which are the basic components of the membrane. The result of this havoc is a loss of suppleness in this barrier of protection and exchange. The enzymes (ATPases) within can no longer create the energy necessary for the cellular factory. Although the excess generates a surplus of calories, it remains unutilised as the cell suffers from paralysis of the intoxicated enzymes. The activity of enzymes depends closely on their lipid environment. Confronted with the wine action, this milieu is highly fragile and delicate.

In small doses, champagne liquefies the fat molecules and activates the work of the enzymes as a biological catalyst. This truly embodies its medicinal virtues, which tradition has utilised in the treatment of minor menstrual discomforts.

With an excessive dosage, enzyme paralysis always occurs following the changes brought about in the cellular membrane. Not only is there no biological benefit to be expected from inordinate consumption, but furthermore there is an accumulation of free radical threatening molecules rich in oxygen capable of burning other enzymes. Our nerve cell are, of course, equipped with enzymes charged with the destruction of free radicals, such as those called 'superoxides dismutases', which capture free oxygen to neutralise it, thus preventing it from harming other enzymes. Unfortunately, alcohol abuse produces an even more toxic waste, acetaldehyde, which precisely inhibits this precious category of superoxide dismutase enzymes. The free radicals then get free rein in their sabotage. The wreckage they cause is exacerbated by damage to the ionic channels, which ensure production of local electrical energy at the level of the membrane.

With respect to these channels, wine has a double action depending on the dosage consumed. In someone who drinks champagne moderately for therapeutic reasons - to calm menses, which might be a bit too abundant and painful, for instance - the ionic calcium content helps to ensure the stability of the cellular membrane, especially in the muscle fibres of the uterus. The arrival of the ions calms the fibres and produces an ample, yet coordinated contraction. Their response to the hormonal and enzymatic messages becomes more efficient and less chaotic. Pain is lessened. The bleeding itself is regularised, thanks to the coordination of the control centres located at the base of the brain. There is a real functional coupling between hormones, enzymes and membranes at all levels of the menstrual organization. It has been possible to deconstruct the mechanism of the systems of surveillance and auto-regulation in the spleen. Wine in small doses triggers the opening of the ionic channels, which can also be observed at the level of the deep nerve centres. The influx of ions raises by one notch the electrical potential of the nerve cell membranes and harmonizes their work.

On the contrary, too much wine, and the enzyme performance is perturbed, as they lose their capacity for mutual assistance, a vital condition for any cellular activity. That is why the onset of pregnancy represents a critical period in which it is adviseable to abstain from champagne, or any alcohol for that matter. The placenta has an extraordinary capacity to transform the slightest trace of ethanol and higher alcohol into acetaldehyde. The work performed by the team of S. Fisher at the University of Cornell has demonstrated the presence of this toxic element in the placenta and foetus when the mother absorbs an important dose of wine (two glasses), or, even worse, whisky. The placenta is extremely vigilant in the protection of the foetus. Its enzymes are hyperactive and destroy all alcohol molecules which they encounter but, in the process, produce even more toxic matter (acetaldehyde) which penetrates the brain of the foetus.

Glucose

Over the past years, biologists have been able to discover the discrete means through which our cells receive or scramble information. This is a very important discovery and which permits an understanding of how they organise their communication, execute the order received or, on the contrary, disobey by committing errors. Much of it rests on sugar molecules arranged on the surface of their membrane, as well as inside the cellular machinery. These sugar formations are of an incredible complexity and their structure varies according to the type of cell and their function. It is sugar links which weave the nervous system of the cell and tissue. But it is not just any kind of sugar. Life requires only one type, indispensable and irreplaceable glucose, the very one synthesised by vine and stored by grapes. It further requires glucose to be in ionic form, carrying an electrical charge that the cell can exploit directly, thanks to its enzymes.

Naturally, all fruits, vegetables and cereals can supply an abundant quantity of glucose, as it constitutes the base of all plant matter. But grape glucose, and especially the one transformed by wine yeast, possesses a precious quality: its energy is not only immediately available to the cell machinery, but it can also be activated and reversed. It means that glucose, with the help of enzymes, can alternatively relinquish electrons to activate the cell and recapture them thereafter. A very thrifty and efficient system requiring a minimum of sugar to avoid clogging up the pipework. This system is quite different from chemical linkage by saturation; the latter occurs in the presence of sugar overload without intervention by enzymes. Once the energy is supplied, the glucose molecules remain glued to the cell structure and end up hindering its activity. That is exactly what happens when consuming too much sugar, or when diabetes ravages the organism by inactive sugar deposits.

Following work by Takashi Muramatsu's team at the New York Medical College, it has become easier to understand the complexity of ionic glucose in the various vital functions of the cell. Practically all molecules of proteins (enzymes, hormones, elements comprizing the cellular structure) are surrounded by an inextricable network of sugars. The set creates mixed molecules called 'glycoproteins'. These elements are furthermore tied to a net, also made of sugars, which ensure communications like a telephone network. The fat molecules of the cell are subjected to similar constraints. They unite with sugar formations to construct glycolipids. On the evidence, sugars are to be found everywhere in the cellular factory. Willy-nilly, the cells are forced to live permanently in this strange compulsory 'honeymoon'. What is the purpose of these sugar networks? It is these very glucoses, in strictly limited quantities, which maintain the organization and harmony between the various parts of the cellular factory. They also carry on the dialogue with adjacent cells. In short, they are the communication agents of the cell. Without their involvement, everything would succumb to chaos and rebellion in an organism as complex as the human body. Thus, at all levels, transmission of the order to be executed must be scrupulously faithful and efficient, without the slightest possibility of an error. This sensitive mission, indispensable to the functional unit, is incumbent on the sugars which must relay messages to the right places, assist in the performance and eventually correct defects. Emission, reception, nourishment, production, repair, recycling, nutrition, coordination, defence, none of the vital functions of the cell can do without them.

One understands the danger if such failures were to happen in our lines of immune defence. Poorly transmitted, received, misinterpreted or executed messages could provoke erroneous responses. Once disorganised, the immune system could manufacture antibodies which, instead of fighting the enemy could attack itself. Auto-immune aberrations are quite frequent in elderly people. The blinded organism produces anti-bodies which destroy their own organs, provoking a sort of biological suicide.

In other circumstances which are far from exceptional, a surfeit of inert, or non-reactive, glucose can trap the small fatty molecules (LDP) of the blood. This leads to deposits, which thicken the arterial wall. Arteriosclerosis takes hold and threatens to shrink and obstruct the small calibre arteries of the heart, brain, eyes and penis.

From this standpoint, glucose is a double-edged sword. All depends on quality and quantity, reversibility and ionic state, and on the capacity to perform multiple and contrary tasks without hindering the functions of the cellular apparatus. That is why dry (and not semi-dry) champagne, containing little sugar, is advised to those requiring a tonic. One glass provides enough to stimulate the organism with a largely sufficient supply of energy.

One of the essential roles that cells expect from glucose, activated by yeasts and mineral elements, is to act as transport. It means that the sugar molecule must know how to perform exchanges with other molecules of the cellular plant, whether enzymes, hormones, proteins, fat or sugar. The sugar, alive and intelligent, must momentarily lock, without fail, onto another molecule to provide it with its energy in the form of electrons. It must then immediately release it to receive other electrons coming from the metallo-enzymes. Glucose, in turn, has its atoms deconstructed while liberating energy in other processes. So, molecule after molecule, the sugar transports to each the necessary energy while recharging its own all the way along. It is for this reason that the glucose molecule must remain free, and not become imprisoned by the molecules it contacts; otherwise it would become inert and hinder the good function of the cellular plant.

When this mechanism is impaired, for whatever reason, glucose becomes inert and the chemical reaction it triggers becomes irreversible. Once paired with a protein or an enzyme, it cannot get rid of it; it is chained to another molecule. Even worse, while attempting to free itself, it will capture other molecules. The errors proliferate and the mess widens. If it happens at the level of a tendon, they will remain clustered together by inter-linkage, woven into sugar structures, which are real prisons. The biological error, in this case, will engender muscle weakness. The contractility and elasticity of the affected ligaments diminishes and muscle stiffness sets in. If it affects the fibres of the artery walls, the artery loses suppleness. Everywhere, the denatured or excessive glucose will create havoc and behave like an enemy instead of acting like a guardian angel. No surprise then if the subject complains about loss of memory, alertness, sleep, energy and even loss of virility.

This is only one of the biological aspects of glucose. The most serious errors take place mainly in the mitochondria, sausage-shaped, which are located in the cell. These formations (organelles) are micro-electric power stations. At the dawn of life, these mitochondria were independent micro-organisms which lived in nature like yeasts and bacteria. These distant cousins still do. And then one day they were captured and domesticated by the cells to produce electricity. That is why these organisms possess, like the nucleus of our cells, their own bit of ADN, proof of their alien origin and long-lasting slave status. Their ADN is, of course, a lot simpler than that of our cells, a lot more fragile too, and not similarly equipped for repairs. The workers in these power plants are, as usual, enzymes charged with seizing oxygen, glucose and calcium to generate current. They convert chemical energy into electric energy. As we age, errors on this bit of ADN accumulate and their operating programme starts getting into a muddle. They lose their generating capacity and efficiency.

Energy crisis. We know something about that. In our case everything turns out for the worse: from muscle to brain, the cells weaken and see their performance decrease. After seventy-five, certain sedentary subjects produce only half the energy they did at forty! These persons find it difficult to endure cold and regulate their production of calories. The energy deficiency has repercussions on their mental and physical activity.

To a certain extent, one can help their capacity of recovery and repair by supplying them, not only with an appropriate diet, but also with glucose and activated mineral elements, in ionic form. These substances help the enzymes charged with repairing the lesions to the ADN according to a determined sequence, which consists first in locating the place where the error is hiding, excising and removing the damaged ADN segment; then, other enzymes copy another programme to replace the old one. Finally, the new segment must be re-inserted in the correct spot. It is as if a page of the encyclopaedia of life had been damaged and one had to remove, repair, and glue it back in its proper place.

This complex mechanism of repair is so delicate that it can be paralysed by nicotine or caffeine. Conversely, high-value nutritive substances stimulate and reinforce it.

It is in solving the enigma of this phenomenon that one realised the truly amazing dietetic qualities of champagne, which has helped so many persons in a weakened state to feel better after a two or three week treatment.

The Process of Hydrolysis

It is a transfer between molecules of positively charged protons and not of negatively charged electrons. Each water molecule of the wine, or any other biological liquid for that matter, is dissociated: on one hand, a half molecule formed by an atom of oxygen tied to an atom of hydrogen (OH-), negatively charged; on the other hand, an atom of hydrogen which has lost its only peripheral electron, its atomic nucleus stripped, constituted by a single proton positively charged.

While the wine ages, yeasts, which have a water molecule that our enzymes use, release two categories of negative (OH-) and positive (H+) ions, which are particularly abundant in champagne.

In a cell, in order to splice a protein for instance, our enzymes use a sharp and quick tool, which is nothing else than a water molecule. It is hydrolysis which allows digestion or dissociation of the long chains of proteins into basic units, amino acids, without recourse to either high temperatures or high acidity, as one does it in industry. At body temperature, in a liquid which is basically neutral (pH 7) and, incredibly fast, the enzymes extract the raw materials (amino acids, fatty acids, simple sugars) from food.

How do they manage to perform such an alchemic trick? Precisely because of the tools based on the hydrogen nucleus: the positively charged proton. They have managed to conquer and master the powerful furnace of the atom to transform it into a blowtorch. An enzyme, such as the pancreatic chymotrypsin, first captures a water molecule and splits it in two: OH- and H+. It then takes the positive ion, which is the hydrogen nucleus, and aims it at a weak spot of the protein chain to dismantle it. At that very spot is located a solitary electron, negatively charged, the weak link in the protein chain. As the enzyme approaches, it activates the target by raising its energy level one notch. In the process, the proton picks up the electron and breaks off the molecule of amino acid from its protein chain. That is the way chymotrypsin breaks down protein to obtain amino acids, supported in this task by zinc (Zn+), which is also a positive ion, to help fuel an alternate reaction.

Over one hundred and twenty digestive enzymes rely on its assistance, as well as that of nickel, cobalt and manganese. The synergy of these elements allows us to understand the wonderful benefits of champagne when drunk in the recommended quantity. Is it a surprise then that a person in a weakened state can recover, without further ado, a feeling of well-being and an appetite, as he can now digest and assimilate food? The production of energy is distinctly improved as it is, through the transfer of protons, that enzymes produce heat and current by breaking up in a similar fashion the energy locked in ATP.

It is in this proton mine that our cells draw the fundamental energy necessary for the operation and maintenance of life.

But it goes as for all good things in life: a benefit in moderation, a poison in excess. Ever wondered why Buddhism, the Middle Way, made moderation and the 'middle of the road', a basic philosophical tenet? 'Ipsa felicitas se, nisi temperat, premit' - 'Boundless felicity, self destructs' said Seneca. Eternal and Universal wisdom!

Illustration Credits

CIVC (Comité Interprofessionel des Vins de Champagne), cover photos, book ends, 32, 36, 42, 60, 62, 80, 84, 98, 101, 108/9, 130.
Mary Evans Library, 16, 26, 27, 28, 29, 78, 85.
Moët Henessy, 11, 41, 64, 65.
Noack Daumier Collection, 17, 22, 114, 119, 124, 126, 129.
Pol Roger Champagne, 105.
Ronald Searle, 48, 76.
Sennep, 70, 103.
UMC (Union des Maisons de Champagne), 8.
Wellcome Library, 16, 35, 40, 43, 46, 52, 55, 58, 68, 69, 83, 87, 91, 92, 97.

Table of Illustrations

p69: lithograph, the young Prince of Wales (later Edward VII) led astray by his nurse.
p70 & 103: drawings by Sennep from Rabelais' Pantagruel.
p78: The God of War, Rata Lange in Der Wahre Jacob, nb.592, 1909.
p83: etching with watercolour by Thomas Rowlanson, 1813.
p85: Dom Perignon, Le Petit Journal, 1914.
p91 & 93: etchings with watercolour, G. Cruikshank, Alfred Crowquill.
p97: etching with watercolour, I. Cruikshank, George Moutard Woodward.
p105: Pol Roger advertisement, Winston Churchill and his favourite champagne. Quote by W.C. in 1917.
p114, 119, 124, 126, 129: lithographs of H. Daumier, Charivari, 1848 to 1856.